An Unfinished Journey

For Heather, without whose inspiration and love the journey would not have begun

Published by The Katharine House Hospice Trust 2007

ISBN 978-0-9555195-0-5

FOREWORD

"The end of my life is turning out to be a very rich and rewarding – even beautiful – time of life. I have discovered that when you face death squarely, you know sharply what it is to be alive. I have learned how to communicate with my family in a way I had never done before. I have understood the damage and waste of anger and the value of forgiveness. I have run my life through my fingers and felt satisfied with how I have lived and what I have done. I am very much alive."

A hospice patient

The UK's hospice movement has been described as one of the greatest innovations of the twentieth century which has revolutionised how those approaching the end of their life, and their friends, families and loved ones, are cared for and supported. It is hard to believe that as little as forty years ago there was very little dedicated and expert care for those whose illness was no longer responsive to curative treatment. Thankfully, the picture is very different now with over two hundred and twenty hospices working in communities across the UK and a growing global movement that is seeing hospice and palliative care services being initiated in some of the most far reaching corners of the world.

Yet the very existence of this now international movement is attributable to the hard work and determination of small groups of individuals who wished to change the way the dying are cared for in their communities. Driven by the desire to change the experience for others, it is a testament to their determination that the care and compassion given by hospice staff and volunteers now touches the lives of around a million people each year across the UK alone.

In putting pen to paper to record his journey, Neil is capturing a very personal experience and perspective that is a critically important part of our understanding of how, exactly, the hospice movement came into being and influenced the society in which we now all live. Neil's story is unique yet it echoes the vision, passion and drive of those others who have followed a similar path. Together they make a rare breed – and one which the world would be all the poorer without.

I am fortunate to have worked with Neil over the years and to have benefited from the stillness and wisdom born of his own painful and remarkable journey. It is important that this story is told and I highly commend it to all.

As Dame Cicely Saunders said "You matter because you are you and you matter to the last moment of your life".

David Praill, Chief Executive, *Help the Hospices*

CONTENTS

Chapter	Page
Introduction	1
First steps – a bunch of amateurs	3
Foundation	6
Reaching out	9
Consolidation	13
The State or not the State	22
Does it matter?	26
Last lap before the Marathon	31
We're off	34
Have we got it right?	40
Funding a local hospice	49
An unexpected role	53
Other voices	59
Almost the last word	101
The last song	104
Envoi	114

INTRODUCTION

"When I heard the last song a journey was contemplated.
The language I knew, but the notes' ethereal echo
spoke of a new tongue to be learnt
and carried over continents of silence in search of a new home –
I'll follow the echo down pathways of eternity."

A memoir has been described as a view of history from within. So I am aware that attempting to write the history of an organisation to which one has a strong attachment is a daunting task because of the danger of seeing events from a blinkered personal perspective. Over twenty years, so many different people have been involved and so many of the facts which comprise this history are theirs that I must first make an apology for anything written in the following pages which might not ring true from the perspective of some readers. In recording these recollections I have received a great deal of help and encouragement from many people but any errors of fact or interpretation that become apparent are mine alone.

In this introduction I will try to answer two questions. Why a hospice? Why a book about the Hospice? The quotation at the head of this section is the title poem from a collection of elegiac writing which formed part of my response in the months immediately following the death of my daughter Katharine in June 1984. Following the echo led to the only possible conclusion that from such a good and positive life something good and positive should follow.

The hospice movement is one of the most beneficial improvements in our society to have developed over the last half century, an important element of civilisation being the quality of the care offered to those who are facing the end of life. Trying to improve the quality of that care for local people seemed, therefore, to be a logical way of following the echo.

But why record the story? In his book "Mutual Aid" published in 1939, Peter Kropotkin asserted that the media and indeed historians offer a distorted depiction of their times by ignoring, or at least omitting to record effectively, the "countless acts of mutual support and devotion" which we all experience. We know that the media chronicles every war and calamity, but we also know that war and calamity are only part of the human experience. Sixty years after Kropotkin, John Major, in his memoirs, put it much more succinctly : "No row, no story".

Pascal described mankind as "both the shame and glory of creation". No-one should be surprised that negative actions have sometimes impinged on this story and feature occasionally, but so much more has been constructive, affirmative, unequivocally positive and heartening, that I believe the story is worth the telling.

I have no literary pretensions in setting down the story and no deep insights will impinge upon the narrative. It is simply the story of what can be achieved when a group of people, with shared objectives and the will to work together, wish to implement a change for the better.

FIRST STEPS – A BUNCH OF AMATEURS

"The dissatisfied dead cannot noise abroad the neglect they have suffered"
Professor J. Hinton

That an eminent doctor could speak thus in the latter half of the twentieth century does a great deal to explain the establishment and growth of the hospice movement and indeed the desire to improve the conditions and environment in which people can experience the end of life has, happily, been a significant feature of our community. What might be called a strong civic society, in which people are willing to do things for each other, has enabled hospices to flourish in the last fifty years.

Of course, hospices have existed for centuries. The purpose of medieval hospices is well known: to provide food and shelter for travellers on the pilgrim routes of Europe. But they could also care for the sick and dying. It seems that the first time the word hospice was applied to an institution created solely for the purpose of the care of the dying was in 1842 when significantly Les Dames du Calvaire established a hospice in Lyon in France. I say significantly because it was female religious orders that established and carried out the caring in the first British hospices at the end of the nineteenth century and early in the twentieth.

But the real growth of the modern hospice movement, with its holistic approach to care, is founded on the work of Dame Cicely Saunders whose St. Christopher's Hospice opened in 1967. Hers is unquestionably an inspirational story which gave significant encouragement to the many who asked the question "If end-of-life care can be enhanced in London, why not everywhere?"

A book on the whereabouts of records retained by hospices shows that frequently the roots of local hospices lie in the catalystic experiences of individuals or small groups of people who wanted the kind of change which was pioneered by Dame Cicely and which would help to eradicate "the undreamt of catalogue of suffering" which the Marie Curie Foundation had uncovered and reported in 1952.

A typical story is of the founding Chairman of a northern hospice who had nursed her husband during his final illness. She mentioned the possibility of a hospice to a friend whose response was to open her handbag, take out a five pound note and hand it over with the comment "There you are, there's your first donation. If you don't do it, you are taking money under false pretences". That a few years after the conversation the hospice was up and running is a testament not only to her tenacity and a great deal of hard work and commitment on the part of the people of that community, but also to Dame Cicely's assertion that "faith can move mountains but it is quicker and more effective if we each pick up a shovel and physically help the process".

Before going on to describe the first steps which we took along the road towards the establishing of Katharine House I want to say that, for the most part, the last twenty years have been an enjoyable experience because of the many supportive, committed and generous people with whom I have been associated. They have outnumbered the sceptics, the doubters and, even more, the opponents.

The Gallup organisation has identified a number of key strengths essential to the success of an embryo project. One such strength, seen to be vital, is vision defined as: "The capacity to create and project beneficial images to be achieved into the future to which the leaders can be dedicated". In the early days our vision of what we wanted to achieve was uncertain but, if we can be considered to have been successful, it is because, however hazily, we were a group of people who had jointly created a vision of a future goal for the benefit of others, which was capable, as it turned out, of inspiring and motivating those whose support and cooperation was necessary for its achievement.

If the previous paragraph appears to be a claim to professionalism, it is not so intended. Members of the group were professionals in their own fields but raising funds and managing projects such as this were beyond our experience. It is interesting to record that, at a meeting in July 1985 with the Chairman of Oxfordshire Health Authority and some of her senior colleagues, one of our number referred to us as "a bunch of amateurs". It was very obvious that they agreed. That meeting was valuable in giving us a clear understanding that our relationship would not necessarily be smooth. The moral, and later personal, support of the Chairman was encouraging but it was obvious that there could be no expectation of support from the Health Authority in any other way. Indeed, in the margins of the meeting I was told to "Stop meddling in things which you do not understand".

In his study of nine hospices entitled "What price Charity", Martin Johnson quotes the General Manager of a different Health Authority who said that

4

hospice trustees "spent a tremendous amount of time becoming educated about hospices…they travel widely and extensively to talk to people, go to conferences…become members of national societies and organisations for hospice care…they become experts in terms of the provision of care….not professionals but experts", confirming perhaps that amateurs are not necessarily the bungling laymen of modern usage of the word but the passionate lovers of their subject as the Latin root *amator* implies. The few words in the quotation describe exactly what we tried to do. Others will judge how successfully. It took several years.

Our first formal meeting took place on 25th October 1984. Nine people were present and a decision was taken to establish The Katharine House Hospice Trust and attempt to create a ten or twelve bed in-patient facility. It was reported by those present that a number of offers to help had been received and it was agreed that a Patron should be sought.

Several weeks prior to this meeting I had announced our intention at a Memorial Concert organised by Katharine's friends, many of whom were, like her, excellent musicians. It was held on what would have been her twenty-first birthday, was a moving occasion and lent resolution to our purpose.

FOUNDATION

*"Until one is committed there is hesitancy, the chance to draw
back, always ineffectiveness. Concerning all acts of initiative
there is one elementary truth the ignorance of which kills
countless ideas and splendid plans: that the moment one
definitely commits oneself then providence moves.*

*All sorts of things occur to help one that would never otherwise
have occurred. A whole stream of events issue from the decision,
raising in one's favour all manner of unforeseen incidents and
meetings and material assistance which no man could have
dreamed would have come his way."*

Goethe

Patsy Edwards had been running sales of antiques and other items in her barn
for some time but, in the summer of 1984, decided to devote the proceeds from
these activities to the Hospice project. Hers was the first tangible contribution
to a concept which she wished to nurture. A sign outside the barn made her
intention public.

We were not aware at this stage that another group of people had also been
discussing the need for hospice care in the locality. This group, members of
which were professionals close to the problems met by those experiencing
cancer, had plans to provide day care for two or three days a week, perhaps in a
rented property. Shortly after the sign was displayed in Sibford Ferris a
member of this group drove through the village. No-one saw the expression on
his face as he digested the message but we are told that it registered surprise.

The two groups met informally for the first time in January 1985 and pooled
their ideas. It was obvious that the group of which I was a member had more
ambitious plans perhaps because we were driven by more personal concerns.
Jeff Chard later wrote "The meeting was the catalyst to my involvement….I
think I became involved because I was caught up with the fervour and
enthusiasm…..what I call the charisma of the hospice".

By this time a Deed of Trust had been drafted and when this was approved by
the Charity Commission in January 1985 it was signed by the people who
became trustees and took on the responsibilities which that implies. A Charity
Commission publication "Milestones" (Regulatory Study 6) published in

December 2003 states "casework experience indicates that trustees are not always accurate in their expectations…..and …..underestimate the complexity of trusteeship". We were in no doubt about the magnitude of the task which we had set ourselves. Our original estimate that we would need, initially, to raise half a million pounds was within weeks revised to one million pounds after we had looked a little more deeply beneath the surface.

A similar mountain to scale had been faced by Cicely Saunders when in 1961 she first approached Albertine Winner who, at the time, was Medical Officer at the Department of Health. Referring to the meeting 20 years later, Dame Winner said that she perceived Cicely Saunders' scheme "wild and madly extravagant, estimated at £350,000". She asked Cicely if she had any money and received the reply "Yes, £500", but that "if it is right, it will happen". That £500 had been left to Dame Cicely in 1948 by David Tasma to be a "window into your home" and he gave a further commission, that he wanted "what is in your heart and in your mind".

Did we have such faith? Perhaps some of us did and we were certainly gratified by the extremely positive signals which we began to receive from many sources within the community. Among the first of these had occurred on Christmas Eve 1984. A group of Katharine's friends, down from their various higher education establishments, went carol singing and had deposited the proceeds of their afternoon in Banbury on the floor of our sitting room. It amounted to £200. But they were more excited by the favourable reactions they had experienced when, for the first time, their listeners heard about the possibility of a local hospice.

Support came from every quarter. Within a few months the Duke of Marlborough, Lord Saye and Sele, Lord Stuart Blanche, Yehudi Menuhin and Paul Eddington had become patrons. The Duke and Lord Saye and Sele, who remain patrons to this day, have been robust supporters in many ways over the years. When I met the founding chairman of St. Leonard's Hospice a few years ago he told me that one of the most daunting experiences of his life had been the moment when he stood on a public platform and announced that an attempt would be made to provide hospice care in York. He was emboldened, he said, by the presence at his side of the Archbishop of York. So this was the second time that Lord Blanche had given his support to a hospice project. Since I have often been asked why Paul Eddington and Yehudi Menuhin had agreed to lend their names, here is the definitive answer. Katharine had attended the same school as the former and, as a keen violinist, had met the latter at a music festival in Southern France.

A period of what sometimes felt like frantic activity now began. Between October 1984 and February 1991 when we moved into the new hospice building, the trustees met 107 times. Building, medical, finance and fundraising sub-committees added a further 68 meetings; the communications group a further 14 and the appeal committee more than 20.

Indicative of the support which the idea received prior to any planned publicity were two telephone calls which I received, one late in 1984, the other later in 1985. The first was from Martyn Gibbs, a member of the committee of the Bray Doyly Housing Association. This organisation, allied to the Society of Friends, had established some semi-sheltered housing for retired people at East House in Adderbury. Martyn, whose daughter was one of Katharine's closest friends, suggested that a four acre field adjacent to East House used as grazing for sheep would be a suitable site for a hospice. We were not aware of the many obstacles which would need to be negotiated if we were to utilise the offer but, when we visited the field, what I can only describe as a tangible sense of numinousness enveloped us. The second call was from a complete stranger who has since become a good friend. Caroline Weatherby spoke of her wish to create a garden for the benefit of potential patients and she tells her own story later in this book.

Many other offers of help and expressions of support convinced us that the perception of need was widely held. We were almost compelled to continue.

REACHING OUT

"Learn to ride a bicycle, you will not regret it if you live!"
Mark Twain

Having established a foundation comprising a group of highly committed people it was now time to test the water in the wider community with some major publicity. We were later criticised for 'going public' at this early stage by several people who had experience of major financial appeals, the received wisdom being that the public need to be given confidence in the project by being shown that a significant proportion of the capital requirement has already been raised from trusts and from individuals and industry approached privately.

This theory is all very well when dealing with capital projects, such as a church roof or an extension to a hospital which would then become the responsibility of the relevant authority. Our project did require initial capital for funding a building but also continuous revenue into the distant future. So we had to take the major risk involved by publicising our plans so early. But what is achieved without risk? In any case we were still naïve.

I think it was Ian McLeod, the former Chancellor of the Exchequer, who corrupted the old adage by saying that "money is the root of all progress". It was true that more money would be required but I do not believe that money necessarily leads to progress of any value. Far more important are such human qualities as the already mentioned vision as well as initiative, creativity, energy and even altruism and the ability to act and think in what has become known in modern parlance "out of the box"! Furthermore, what about *eureka* moments?

Thus we did not embark upon a love affair with money. Years before the current Chancellor of the Exchequer embarked upon a love affair with prudence we had already begun to develop a close relationship with her. English does not have an idiomatic expression like the Italian "Pozzo di San Patrizio", a reference to a costly well which was never used. Its meaning, however, is applicable. We did not intend to continuously demand and swallow money without producing a worthwhile result within an agreed budget.

Taking a cautious line was quite natural to us but perhaps also we were influenced by a feeling that a society which shrugs its shoulders at those who perpetrate massive overspends on public projects, and often rewards them with 'golden handshakes' and honours, would not look so kindly on a bunch of failed amateurs. We also knew that we were operating in a community which had witnessed the demise of a project to create a theatre and we were, all too frequently, compared. Furthermore, we had read Ann Robertson's memoir about the founding of the Pilgrim's Hospice in Canterbury in which she had related a story of the Roman Catholic priest who had converted a house in Liverpool to offer care to the dying with no support from the NHS. At the end of some weeks there was not enough money to pay the working staff but the priest always made up the shortfall by touring the pubs on a Friday evening, always successfully. The personal bearing of such risk gives one a powerful reason for exercising caution.

From our growing knowledge base we were aware that the average length of time taken to establish a voluntary hospice, from concept to realisation by the provision of services, was about seven years, with a range of three to a daunting fifteen years. Several months after the conception of our idea we needed an attention capturing event.

Hundreds of people cycle from Lands End to John o'Groats every year so it was not a very original stunt which we chose. But it is true that Einstein had thought a great deal about the theory of relativity while cycling and perhaps had even had a *eureka* moment while in the saddle. At the time of planning the ride, I had been seconded to Warwick University Education Department as a visiting tutor and was undaunted when a colleague in the mathematics department calculated that I would need to press on the pedals several million times. Because, if I lived, what positive Einsteinian thoughts might I have while occupied by pedalling? Better still, if the Chairman of Cherwell District Council and the Mayor of Banbury could be persuaded to participate then publicity would be assured. So we were very gratified indeed when Brent Prestidge and Helen Gibbs agreed to meet the nine cyclists at Banbury Cross, a third of the way through our journey, on a sunny Saturday in August 1985. It was extremely heartening to have such strong civic support. Another brick had been placed in the foundations and Chairmen and Mayors have accepted a Vice-Presidency of Katharine House and been supportive in a variety of ways ever since. A street collection had been approved but our parade around the town led by a Scottish piper perched on the platform of an open truck had not. In those less regulated times, it caused only amusement, requests for more information and offers of help. The event did not raise the one pound per pedal stroke, which someone had suggested it could, but the more modest sum of £3,000. Here I must mention an early example of the contribution made by local businesses. David Grasby, a local coach operator, provided a coach and driver to transport us to Lands End, accompany us to John o'Groats and bring us home again making no charge.

As an aside, I will mention here that in August 1986, three of us cycled from Banbury Cross to the Leaning Tower of Pisa, raising £1,000. I fully recommend spending thirteen days cycling to Italy. It is an excellent way to lose weight (a stone in my case) and to gain the physical fitness required to continue the struggle. The experience was so enjoyable that I have ever since been sceptical about the motives of those who participate in charity challenges which are currently so much in vogue. But 'good luck' to them anyway!

Having just read of an insurance company which issued a two page risk assessment form asking what hazards were likely to be met on a ten-mile sponsored walk for a village hall, which specified hazards such as rabbit holes, overhanging branches and wet surfaces, I will add that we did not carry out risk assessments and I ask the question "Why have we allowed ourselves as a society to be drawn into such stupidity?".

The publicity generated by the 1985 cycle ride began to bear fruit immediately. Over forty offers of support led to the establishment of a semi-formal organisation of 'Friends' groups in localities across the perceived catchment area of the proposed hospice. Each was led by a volunteer; some acted as distributors of information, whilst others, twelve in number, led significant fundraising teams. No doubt the motives of these trail-blazers were varied but having met them all as well as hundreds of others who have been involved as volunteers over the past twenty years, I believe that all subscribed to the moral imperative that we should all try to live our lives as an endeavour to leave the world a little better than we found it. I am equally certain that none of them will have been familiar with some fairly recent research which appears to indicate that volunteering prolongs life.

These pioneers distributed our first newsletter, raised money and generally 'talked-up' the hospice idea. Many of the original group leaders remain supporters to this day, and one group, originally based in Bicester, continues to function, having established a number of highly successful annual events.

At the same time we began to receive requests for speakers to enlighten a whole range of clubs, societies, church groups and schools. Over time more than three hundred such talks were requested. It was encouraging that so many people wanted to know about our plans and their subsequent fund raising activities laid a very firm foundation in the community. Of course we never knew what to expect at these gatherings. One speaker prefaced her talk by saying that she did not intend to speak for long, only to hear a relieved voice respond "I should hope not, we've got Bingo tonight". When we spoke to these groups it was to explain what we were trying to achieve and frequently, if we were sufficiently persuasive, a promise of support was offered or an immediate donation made. But I recall my own experience of speaking to a group for half an hour, answering questions for a further half hour, listening to a highly complimentary vote of thanks, and feeling very encouraged when the chairman announced a collection for the week's charity. Unfortunately, it was not the charity which I had been championing.

However, the experience of 1985 showed that what had appeared at the beginning of the year to be *terra incognita* was in fact fertile ground ready to be ploughed. A precursor perhaps of some research carried out by Centris and published by the Home Office in 1993 which showed that the most dynamic local voluntary activity takes place in small towns.

CONSOLIDATION

"Resolute to the point of madness"
F. W. West

During 1986, 1987 and 1988, a number of themes was pursued at a frustrating rate, now accelerating, now apparently retarded, but enthusiasm was undimmed as people rallied to the cause. First amongst these themes was a desire to provide a positive service to support those in need of the help which was our *raison d'être.*

The National Society for Cancer Relief had been founded in the early part of the nineteenth century by Douglas Macmillan as a response to his own family's experience of providing end-of-life care for his father. We knew that this organisation, today known as Macmillan Cancer Support, funded specialist nurses to work alongside other health care professionals to enhance end-of-life experience. Further investigation taught us that Macmillan funding of these posts was only for three years and that the posts would not be established if subsequent funding could not be guaranteed. In most cases, we learnt, the National Health Service, through Area Health Authorities, provided this guarantee.

Our first meeting with the National Society for Cancer Relief in May 1985 led to acknowledgement of the need for two nurses based in Banbury and a promise to meet with us again together with representatives of the Health Authority. There is no doubt that the Area Health Authority acknowledged the need but was not prepared to take up the funding at the end of three years. At last a compromise was reached. We would become responsible for funding the service during years four and five which would give the authority time to plan its financial involvement. Since the first nurse was not appointed until September 1989 and the second in December of that year, it will be understood that the negotiations to reach this agreement were long and difficult and a number of years later the story had an ending which was unexpected and highlighted our earlier naivety. However, when the nurses were appointed, we were pleased as two very different organisations began to develop co-operative procedures.

Another theme was a desire to understand and benefit from the multiplicity of Grant Making Trusts by convincing them of the value of our cause. Some of these Trusts had originated in mediaeval times. I once lived in a village where there was a Trust founded in the fifteenth century by a John Kimble who, as a wandering orphan, had been befriended and cared for by the ancestors of the twenty-first century beneficiaries who now in childhood receive a grant of money to buy secondary school uniform and in old age receive a sack of coal each year. We, however, needed to persuade more wealthy Trusts that we were serious and viable. Poring over newly acquired directories of Trusts, we were impressed by the range and variety of their histories and policies. One Trust which had originally been founded to support the victims of piracy and derived its income from the rent of some allotments which it owned, was now very wealthy because the seventeenth century allotments had become the site of some of the most valuable property in London. Indeed, in due course, that Trust along with many others did donate funds to Katharine House.

But before we had worked out a strategy to enable us to pursue this idea, one of those events occurred that Goethe had predicted. Heather Gadsby, through an interest in yoga, met someone who was not only interested in the hospice project but also had a strong family connection with the founder of a Grant Making Trust. It gave us enormous encouragement when the Appledore Trust donated £100,000 and more in subsequent years.

The lesson from this experience was that personal contacts could be of considerable value. In this context, we were very fortunate now to be introduced to the Honourable Peter Ward who agreed to establish a committee to pursue this form of fundraising. The committee met for the first time in May 1987 and proved to have members with useful contacts with Trusts that over time proved to be very successful. This was the 'warm approach' but 'cold calling' could be equally successful and this I took on myself. For this it was necessary to understand fully the policies of the various Trusts and to try to ensure that applications were appropriate, detailed and succinct. Again, over time, this activity succeeded. Eventually more than three-quarters of a million pounds was donated by more than a hundred Trusts.

Alongside this activity, John Bridgeman, who at this time was Managing Director of Banbury's largest company Alcan, agreed to establish a local business committee which led to a further stream of donations, some of which were in kind and of such appropriateness that they could be incorporated into the Hospice building. These included windows, kitchen equipment, carpets, curtains and even an electronic control system for central heating and the plaster for the walls. Peter Ward owned a brick company and his generosity knew no bounds, so that every brick subsequently used to build the hospice was donated by Baggeridge.

Another activity taken on by Peter Ward's committee was the organisation of events. The first of these, a charity auction, proved to be highly successful thanks to the Duke of Marlborough for permitting the use of Blenheim Palace, and Tim Rootes and his team for drawing support from a wide range of people to organise and contribute so that the end result following the auction conducted by Christies was £180,000 for Katharine House including a donation of £60,000 from the Variety Club of Great Britain towards the cost of the family rooms which are an important part of the Hospice today. It was at this event that I first met Princess Diana who at the time was still Princess of Wales. In his memoir, Douglas Hurd says of Princess Diana that "she had that combination of beauty and charm that melts men's bones". It is difficult to disagree but I would add that her interest in people was genuine and sincere. At Blenheim she was asked by Heather Gadsby if she would in due course formally open Katharine House. She agreed and watching her with patients several years later in October 1991, one observed a true rapport.

Race evenings at Stratford-upon-Avon and Towcester and a range of musical events across the district, which were all grist to the mill of this hard-working committee, followed in quick succession and added both publicity and money.

A major event outside the committee was the major coup of securing the M40, just before it opened, for a fundraising event. This took the form of a AAA's authorised 10 km run with an associated fun run. The first and last time a mass participation event was held on the motorway. Cycling along the motorway with the official AAA's course measure is a pleasure I still recall especially when driving on the same stretch of busy road now. The event which also involved the Red Arrows Aerial Display Team and acrobatic parachutists is a good example of how pleasure has become irrevocably associated with the process of raising funds for good causes.

During these years we visited twenty other hospices in different parts of the country and it was at this time that I began to feel that there was something special about what is now often referred to as the hospice movement which was then an even looser association of individual organisations than it remains today, although perhaps change is imminent. We were always made incredibly welcome, our questions always answered with openness and an obvious desire to share and spread philosophy and practical ideas and we always left with enhanced confidence. I now believe that the hospice phenomenon is one of the most positive aspects of our society contributing greatly to the strength and cohesion of local communities.

Our sub-committees had different briefs for these visits and one was to look at the idea of charity shops that we knew some hospices had established. How to introduce such a fundraising stream was not difficult and made easier by the advice that was willingly given during visits, but taking the plunge was something about which we hesitated. Minutes of Trustee meetings show over several years that we prevaricated. A number of premises became available but the negative factors involved with them always seemed to outweigh the positive ones. It is not difficult to read between the lines to see that committing funding to such a venture was the problem. What would be the public reaction to spending money on a shop before service provision was established? When suitable premises did become available so did the up-front funding. A local Grant Making Trust gave £10,000 partly in the form of a zero interest loan for the express purpose of establishing our first charity shop which we did in May 1988. We need not have been nervous. A volunteer manager, who stayed in post for five years, and a team of other volunteers brought instant success to the venture so that when, in later years, expansion seemed appropriate, we expected and achieved success so that our shops, which are not considered to be a trading activity, contribute significantly to the costs of providing hospice care.

At a later date, we were approached by representatives of the NHS hospice in Oxford for advice on fundraising, and a collaborative scheme evolved. I am not aware of this sort of activity between a voluntary and an NHS organisation existing previously. It did flourish for a time with shared charity shops in Bicester and Oxford but soon floundered, not because of management disagreements but because volunteers did not fully support the concept. In the end we decided to abort the arrangement and take one shop each. This, I think, says a great deal about the passion that volunteers bring to the local organisation which they support, as well as about the perceptions held by members of the public about what constitutes a local charity. It is interesting to note that the regular reports on charity shops published by Charity Finance Magazine show that shops supporting local charities, and these are usually voluntary hospices, consistently outperform those of the national charities with regard to profit as a percentage of turnover. We were very careful, for two reasons, to ensure that our shops were a means of selling on donated goods, thus ensuring that they were not classified as trading outlets as defined by

Customs and Excise, and did not compete with local traders. Later a letter in the local press complained about the competition from eleven charity shops and the effect that these were having on the writer's business. I contacted the writer with a carefully prepared statement about our activities and the benefits that accrued from those activities to the local community. Expecting a difficult confrontation, I was met with the response "Oh, I didn't mean Katharine House".

At the risk of contradicting my earlier claim that money was not the be all and end all of our thinking, I will refer to a number of other fundraising endeavours, while emphasising that these were always accompanied by clear explanations of our aims and objectives to enhance end-of-life care.

Three direct mailings supported by Paul Eddington, Martyn Lewis and Kenneth Kendall spread the word to every home in the district and resulted in the recruitment of many long term supporters. The first mail shot was outsourced to a company that specialised in this kind of activity. We waited anxiously for the expected returns but they did not materialise within the time scale predicted. Fortunately this was not because of the failure of what we considered to be a carefully worded appeal for support but because of a postal strike in Nottingham. Subsequent mailings, one jointly with the aforementioned Oxford hospice, were handled by volunteers in a local independent school that was kindly loaned for the purpose during school holidays. Envelope stuffing, accompanied by conversation and tea, is an essential element in the developmental path of any charity. It is amazing how quickly half a million pieces of paper can be shifted.

During this period, no stone was left unturned to disseminate the message and encourage financial support. Ronnie Barker lent his large personality to help us to collect and convert foreign coins, something which was highly successful until the advent of the euro. Kim Hartman (Helga from "Allo Allo") became involved in our efforts to encourage donations through 'Give as you Earn', a form of giving which has not been as successful for us or indeed nationally as the Chancellor who introduced the concept had hoped. Kim also opened the aforementioned Oxford shop. Hedli Nicklaus of Archer's fame placed the first coin in a mile of coins which grew along the main street in Bloxham. Norman Painting, also of Archers' fame, opened our first Charity shop.

As I have indicated our shops were not technically trading but we knew that most long established charities did trade, usually through associated trading companies. Our first venture into this activity did not follow the tried and tested route of a Christmas Catalogue. Instead, thanks to an idea from a supporter, we took the unusual step of selling our own label wine, washing up liquid and cakes. This strange assortment of products was the result of support for the idea by S H Jones Wine Limited, Cleenol and Meg Rivers Cakes, all of whom supplied these products and were willing to forego any profit. A separate company, Jowins Limited which was bought off the shelf and which later metamorphosed into Katharine's Cupboard Limited, was the medium for these activities which unfortunately were not to be a long term success because of logistical problems. We just did not have the time or the manpower so the Company was removed from Companies House Register. A further misfortune was that when we did ultimately want to trade again by establishing the Christmas Catalogue we simply forgot to reinstate the Company. It was as simple as that. But at the end of the year, on submitting accounts to Companies House, we realised that we had not followed the correct bureaucratic process with the result that I had to swear an affidavit before a bewigged and robed Judge. Fortunately, I could swear with absolute honesty that all the profits from Katharine's Cupboard activities had indeed passed to the charity but it was a salutary lesson, though one from which I have not necessarily learnt. The imperative of getting the job done for the benefit of the organisation and those for whom it cares has, I know, led me in some circumstances to be more impetuous than it is bureaucratically correct to be. I do not regret this "thinking with the blood" as Kipling might have called it.

The range of fundraising activities was fascinating to someone whose previous ideas had been limited to jumble sales. For example, a larger than life teddy bear donated by its young owner (it was so big that perhaps she was afraid of it) was auctioned at the cattle market by Midland Marts fetching £500 and, at the time, rumour had it that there were enquiries about the availability of "straws" so that Rumbo's genes could be introduced into the strain of local cattle. A water polo team raised funds by playing non-stop for 24 hours and entered the Guinness Book of Records because of that achievement. One of the Trustees stayed to offer encouragement throughout the 'game', an act which was symptomatic of the commitment needed and given. Audrey, The Lady Wardington, edited a series of books which are described elsewhere. An auction of penny cheques signed by the great and the good raised £3,500 and surprisingly politicians' autographs were more popular than those of comedians.

Through the Duke of Marlborough I was able to meet with Richard Branson to try to elicit his support. He explained that his charitable activity was directed towards the relief of causes which were not held very high in public esteem, citing drug abuse as an example. He did provide some airline tickets for raffles, but was quite forthright in his opinion that I did not need his help since "you have the passion to carry it through". When Katharine House eventually opened, I received a letter from Richard Branson pointing out that he had been right. A supporter of what we were trying to do offered to arrange a meeting with Robert Maxwell but fortunately, with hindsight, I did not get beyond his front office which was inhabited by guardians who never mentioned his name but always referred to him as "the publisher".

Fundraising has to be in the limelight thriving on the oxygen of publicity but much of the activity during this period was about ensuring that other important parts of the foundation of the edifice, in both meanings of that word, were in place. The route towards the achievement of any significant aspiration is often made easier if one can concentrate, at timely moments, on small interim objectives while keeping the bigger picture in view. But how were we to find the time to achieve that timely single-minded concentration? F. W. (Knocker) West, quoted at the head of this section, was not only my headmaster but also my rugby football coach, who espoused the view that "being resolute to the point of madness" was the characteristic required of a wing forward. Since I did not graduate from the house to the school team, it seems that I did not have sufficient of the quality required for that purpose. But improving end-of-life care was a more worthwhile cause and I claim, without embarrassment, that my resolve that the project should succeed overcame the madness of the decision that I now took in July 1987 so that I could devote all my energies to the Hospice project. Retirement at the age of fifty two on a reduced pension was daunting but was in retrospect one of my better life decisions. My own resolve was strengthened by that of Heather, my wife, whose confidence and certainty were invaluable.

The first interim objective was to find somewhere to work and following a brief period in an office donated by local Estate Agents, Ankers, we moved into a small suite of rooms donated by Crest Hotels in their headquarters building in Banbury which became our base until February 1991 when we moved into the new hospice. Our first employee was the first of many successful ones, organising the office very efficiently and moreover having exactly the right understanding of what we were trying to achieve. She thus became an excellent point of contact for the many members of the public for whom the office was the focal point of our activities.

The site had been promised but now detailed negotiations leading to a leasehold agreement were undertaken with the result that we have a 125-year lease at what, by any comparison, is a peppercorn rent for the land. Hallett Design had been interested in the project from day one and had participated in many of the hospice visits, so Katharine House is an amalgam of the better points, as we saw them, of existing hospices. When planning consent was applied for it was only after every effort had been made to ensure that every question and every possible pitfall had been anticipated. For example, we needed permission to link into a new sewage system that was being created for Banbury Business Park (a fortuitous coincidence), and the appropriate leasehold agreement had to be in place. We also needed to ensure that our immediate neighbours had been informally consulted and were happy with our plans. A major delay was caused by the snail pace of bureaucratic decision-making while it took eighteen months to persuade the Department of Transport to agree the position of road access to the site.

Communication with our supporters and with the general public was vital. We became aware that one Service Club had suspended its support when at a crucial time in its decision making process no progress with the hospice project had been observed. But progress was inexorably being made. In October 1987, four months after my retirement, we were able to announce that planning consent had been granted. Several months later robust staffing plans and costings had been transferred from 'back of envelope' scribble to modern spreadsheets. They must have been robust because they survived the scrutiny of the Executive Directors of the Wolfson Foundation and other trusts. Our Newsletters first published in June 1985 became a vital element in the dissemination of information. Successively edited by Alan Overton, Ken Wortelhock, Tony Brace and myself, Katharine House News is now, many years later, in the capable hands of our recently established Fundraising Office, which has brought a happy exuberance to the publication. Newsletters remain an excellent way of communicating with our supporters and our mailing list now numbers more than 12,000. Public meetings also played an important role, giving Trustees face-to-face opportunities to proselytise to potential new supporters. Well-known practitioners of palliative medicine, such as Dr. David Frampton and Dr. Sheila Cassidy (famous for other reasons too), generously travelled to these meetings to offer a deeper perspective on the role of hospices in society. David mystified his audience by displaying, as people entered the lecture room, a slide showing a pile of scrap cars. It was seen to be a powerful metaphor as his talk unfolded.

It is difficult in a few brief paragraphs to give more than a flavour of the range of issues which had to be pursued through broad-brush discussion and by addressing detailed minutiae, and I have nothing but praise for the small group of people whose commitment, tenacity and, yes, patience achieved our first objectives.

There were times during this period when the level of patience required was difficult to contain. One of my trustee colleagues, reflecting on trusteeship, had written in a 1987 newsletter "One of the vital pre-requisites for being a Trustee is patience. For those of us not fully equipped with an abundance, it has been force-feeding. The amount of thought, of planning, of talking and meetings, of persuasion and discussion, of letters and waiting, of red-tape and regulations, but above all of waiting, is formidable". However, while at the beginning of 1986 £35,000 had been raised and we were still looking across a dimly lit chasm of ignorance, by the end of 1988 we had, to use an agricultural or horticultural metaphor (take your pick), shaken every tree within reach (and attempted to pick fruit from some which had remained beyond our grasp) and had reaped a fine harvest which was a clear idea of the shape of the service that we wanted to provide and being on the verge of an announcement that £1 million had been raised.

THE STATE OR NOT THE STATE?

"What can society action – not the State on its own, not individuals on their own, but all of us together?"

Tony Blair

"Shared responsibility is the hallmark of a civilised society"

David Cameron

During the period described in the previous section we had been invited to fundraising events organised by many clubs and societies in order to receive the proceeds and had frequently shared these proceeds with representatives of the local hospital which was raising funds to rebuild an Accident and Emergency facility, something which we all agreed was needed. It is perhaps appropriate therefore to say something here about the relationship between the voluntary and statutory sectors.

Voluntary effort has historically made a major contribution to the development and growth of social and medical services to the great benefit of the population. A wide range of philanthropic organisations was founded in the nineteenth century to provide a range of benefits which were not otherwise available to those perceived to be in need.

But the reforming Liberal Government of 1906, which one historian has claimed was the first great radical government in British history, believed that there were limits to this kind of provision and moved the emphasis towards public action. "Providing for the aged and the deserving poor" was a Lloyd George mantra. The Labour Government of 1945 hastened the process, agreeing with Aneuran Bevan's belief that volunteerism was "a patch quilt of local paternalism". Indeed, Richard Crossman later described the left's views on philanthropy during the inter-war years as an "odious expression of social oligarchy and church bourgeois attitudes" and that voluntary hospitals maintained by flag days were "detested".

It is true that the 'quilt' was too small and concentrated over those areas where volunteerism was most prevalent so the equity of access to services that followed the foundation of The National Health Service was welcome. But it is interesting to note that the voluntary institutions, which were in effect nationalized, included over a thousand voluntary hospitals. The voluntary management of one such hospital commented that "we may not have the wealth of government, the power to command, but we do have a priceless asset, that, as a people, we want to maintain democracy, not only in a parliamentary, but in a social way".

But none of this inhibited voluntary action in the twentieth century. There are many examples of this kind of action, and the enhancement of end-of-life care is a fine one.

Currently, there are 189 hospices providing specialist palliative care managed, and largely funded by, local charities in the United Kingdom. They provide almost 2,500 beds while the NHS provides just under 700. Voluntary organisations also provide home care, day care, hospital support and in some cases, other specialist care such as lymphoedema clinics. So it can be seen that, with the growth of the hospice movement, there is an important role for volunteerism where the State is unable or unwilling to provide adequate end-of-life care.

However, since 1980 voluntary effort has also become deeply embedded in state institutions. The Health Services Act of 1980 paved the way for a significant blurring of the boundaries between voluntary and state organisations by empowering health authorities for the first time to raise funds from the public, so charity has come to play an important role in today's NHS. More significantly, the Act allowed health authorities to employ exchequer funds to finance fundraising, which left the voluntary sector at a distinct disadvantage. It is interesting to note that in the late 1980's, fundraising expenditure under Section 5 of the 1980 Act doubled each year, and there was a significant increase in the number of appeals. It is probably true that the appeal which illustrated the situation most clearly was the success of The Great Ormond Street Children's Hospital Wishing Well Appeal, which raised £54,000,000 in under 5 years. This was the first time since the NHS was established that charitable funds had been used to pay for the building of a public hospital, rather than paying for extras in the patient and staff welfare field. Further NHS reforms in 1991 next drove a coach and horses through the concept that charity paid for extras so that NHS Trusts needed to have no misgivings about raising charity funds to subsidise core services. Indeed a survey carried out in 1993 found, for example, that Special Baby Units across the country had 66% of their equipment funded by charity while in nine hospitals the figure was 100%.

But we operate in a confused and confusing political environment.

While the NHS took advantage of the freedom given to them by the 1980 Act, voluntary organisations were guided by The Charity Commission view, which was that "trustees cannot normally use charity funds to pay for services that a public body is legally required to provide at the public expense. However, trustees may use charity resources to supplement what the public body provides". This advice was still effective as recently as 2004. The Charity Commission also advised charities in their publication, 'Charities and Contracts', not to enter into contracts "to deliver a service which the public body is required to provide" and also advised charities not to agree to "fill a gap" in a service which is not properly funded by the Government. These are strong words that could have had an inhibiting effect on the actions of trustees who were keen to develop hospice services, but many refused to be hamstrung.

Some of the mist cleared in September 2000 when the Government's 'Cancer Plan' was published. This emphasised the Government's belief that "all patients should have access to the specialist palliative care advice and services which they need" and the document further promised additional investment to enable the NHS "to make a realistic contribution to the costs hospices incur in providing agreed levels of service". But "realistic contribution" was not defined.

The next episode in the confusing saga was the announcement in early 2005 that charitable status had been granted to two leisure services bodies, which had previously it seems, been part of local authorities. I queried one of the opinions on which the decision to grant charitable status to these two bodies was based, namely, that "it was accepted as good charitable purpose to relieve the community from general or local taxation".

Part of the reply to my query is quoted here:

"Gifts to relieve the community from general or local taxation have long been recognised in charity law, as charitable purposes, on the basis that such gifts are patriotic". This goes back to The Charitable Uses Act of 1601 which the court uses for guidance to determine what purposes are charitable. The 1601 Act states purposes including "the aid or ease of poor inhabitants concerning payments of 15ths, setting out of soldiers and other taxes". Although it may seem that the relief of taxation is charitable because of the relief of the poor, the courts have been clear that poverty is **not** required for the relief of taxation to be charitable. The courts have decided that gifts for the relief of taxes to reduce the National Debt and in the reduction or aid of the rates are all charitable.

I am not a historian, nor even it seems a particularly well-informed member of the public, so I was rather surprised by that new-found knowledge. I then pointed out that the statement advising trustees not to use charity funds to pay for services that a public body is required to provide at the public expense was incompatible with the interpretation of the 1601 Act. This has been acknowledged and guidance for trustees will be updated.

Even more recently the Treasury has taken the view that charities which provide services for the benefit of the public[1] should claim full cost recovery, and for hospices, 2008 had been targeted as the date to achieve that objective but it now seems certain that the reality will fall very short.

Does any of this matter?

---

[1] The Charities Act ended its journey through parliament in November 2006 without defining "public benefit". I foresee continuing confusion.

DOES IT MATTER? An attempt to answer the question

Never doubt that a small group of committed citizens can change the world.
Indeed it is the only thing that ever has.

Margaret Mead

There are currently approaching 200,000 charities registered with the Charity Commission. Each charity will have a group of committed citizens as its Trustees. The achievements of these organisations cover a whole range of activities which have enabled the hungry to be fed, the homeless to be housed, children to be nurtured, birds and animals to be protected, the disabled and oppressed to be supported, cures for diseases sought and environments to be rescued. Indeed, an A to Z of charitable activity would leave few letters unused. Without exception the establishment of a charity has grown out of a sense of dissatisfaction and this is especially true of the hospice movement which has developed caring services at the end of life at a level and of a quality previously unknown.

In many ministerial pronouncements over many years tribute has been paid to the activities of the voluntary sector and the contribution it makes to the wellbeing of society. Indeed, I have a pile of letters from Government Ministers stemming from my time as Chairman of The Forum of Chairmen of Independent Hospices specifically extolling the virtues of voluntary hospices. It is interesting to note that in the Cabinet Office Cross Cutting Review published in 2003 the following statement was made: "In contracting with the voluntary sector, Government must ensure that regulation is proportionate and the independence of the sector is recognised. The greater the regulation, the greater the risk that the best features of the sector are smothered". At the Labour Party Conference in 2005 Hazel Blears (who earlier, as a Health Department Minister, had announced significant extra short term ring-fenced funding for charitable hospices) while discussing the voluntary sector's "public services agenda" explained that she "did not want the voluntary sector to be like the public sector" since it was about "engaging ordinary people in a chance to shape their own futures and their own destinies". These pronouncements are a tacit acknowledgement that the independence of the voluntary sector is valuable and that it does have some features which are different and worth preserving.

Hazel Blears has alluded to one positive feature, the involvement of people, but we need a much broader definition if we are to reach a clearer understanding of what is of value and therefore what to preserve. Charity can be defined as kindness, goodwill, compassion, benevolence and altruism and a perusal of various dictionary definitions of the word *voluntary* indicates that voluntary action is perceived to be a form of energy deriving from freewill. It is said to have a moral purpose and is exercised independently. I believe that all these elements feature in voluntary action which I define as the independent, spontaneous action of individuals or groups acting for the benefit of communities of which they are part whether local, national or international; the flexibility which can be applied to such actions while focusing firmly on the vision and the drawing in of more people to altruistic endeavour. However, perhaps we, and I include myself in this, have fallen into a trap by referring to a voluntary sector with the implication that the positive human qualities to which I have referred are confined only to the group of people who work with voluntary organisations, something which is manifestly untrue. But if we look at voluntary organisations as opposed to the people within them we can begin to see some differences. Voluntary organisations have independent origin, are self governing, are independent financially and of course are not for profit. With characteristics like those they certainly do not resemble public bodies.

Now we face the real conundrum. Voluntary action is not a materialistic energy but as it becomes more structured and is provided by larger and larger voluntary organisations economic factors begin to play a more important role and as many voluntary organisations take on roles which are seen to be the responsibility of Government, with or without the encouragement of Government (though now much more likely to be the former), one must ask the question "What is the point of a charity?".

Over recent years a constantly recurring theme in the debate has been the claim that charities provide added value. In 2003 Stuart Etherington, Chief Executive of the National Council for Voluntary Organisations (NCVO), outlined a number of ways in which added value could be assessed and some of these ideas can be applied to voluntary hospices. Voluntary hospices certainly provide specialist niche services which are not otherwise available to a local population. They have a good knowledge of local need usually gained from the experiences which probably led to the founders' dissatisfaction. Charities can be flexible and are often willing to take risks by bypassing bureaucratic regulations and in my experience can do so without putting any individual at significant risk. Being a catalyst for change is another of Stuart Etherington's added value claims. Voluntary hospices are certainly able to affirm this. Each voluntary hospice has established services which were not previously available and three years ago the Government acknowledged that it had some catching up to do. The Cancer Plan stated that "the provision of palliative care services is uneven across the country. It has not been given the priority it deserves by the NHS which has for too long regarded specialist palliative care as an optional extra. The NHS has relied upon the goodwill and funding of charities. Hospices have rightly argued that the NHS should invest more in palliative care services". A categorical admission of guilt with a promise to do better.

Strengthening civic society is another benefit which accrues from voluntary activity. Two years ago I was asked if professionals would be appointed to carry out the tasks currently undertaken by volunteers. My questioner was, I think, surprised when my reply was an unequivocal no. It was no because I believe that volunteers bring something of themselves into the organisation and are a vital link with the wider community creating a valuable symbiotic relationship.

The involvement of individual volunteers can be for a variety of reasons, pure altruism for example and I never cease to be impressed and encouraged by the sheer goodness of the voluntary contributions, by people who seem to subscribe to Tom Paine's view that "my religion is to do good", which I have witnessed. But is it too far fetched to wonder if some charities, and voluntary hospices would be a good example, are in some way akin to the nineteenth and early twentieth century mutual societies? I am not suggesting that supporters of voluntary hospices are all Oddfellows or Foresters who give their support in the conscious expectation of future benefit though it is undoubtedly true that many of them will receive some benefit. Rather perhaps they at least subconsciously subscribe to the view expressed in 1909 by the Grand Master of the Manchester Unity of Oddfellows that "smothering voluntary individual effort and relying entirely on the State" would not eradicate the evils which the Society existed to address, a view which is at odds with that expressed by William Blake over two hundred years earlier when he argued that charity, however admirable, is wrong because it delays reform and perpetuates economic injustice. I think the Grand Master was right.

Finally charitable activity operates solely for the benefit of those in need of the services. For voluntary hospices those who need end-of-life care are our priority. We have no political agenda and I can assure readers that Katharine House has no shareholders.

There is a Chinese (I think) saying which argues that the colour of the cat, be it black or white, is of no consequence as long as it catches the mouse. Using that contention perhaps the answer to the question is that it does not matter. But, as voluntary organisations begin to take on more public service delivery and are thus in effect being paid by the State for what the State believes to be necessary rather than fulfilling the passionate desires of their founders to make a difference, I hope that the result will not be the extinguishing of the fire in the belly which has been such a powerful driving force in the development and growth of voluntary organisations with the danger that innovation will be stifled and independence sacrificed on the altar of regulation.

Perhaps the greatest threat to the flame is the inexorable march of regulation. I am, I think, in good company in expressing my concern. As long ago as 1908, in his electoral address to his Dundee constituents, Churchill wrote "officials now look upon humanity through innumerable grills and pigeon holes and over innumerable counters – all saying tickets please". I do not argue that there should be no regulation. We must do all we can to inhibit the greed and occasional evil which rises to the surface of society, and I certainly believe that life should have been made more difficult for the person, perhaps apocryphal, who attempted to raise money for the widow of the Unknown Soldier. But I do think that regulation can become an uncreative discipline which stifles action and I do not believe that the establishment has the monopoly of wisdom or even, sometimes, of common sense.

In yet another speech by a Government Minister, David Milliband told the NVCO in 2006 that he wanted voluntary organisations to continue to be "advocates, campaigners and protestors, the thorn in the side of Government and the establishment". So I await with interest the conclusions of the Government's *Reduction of the Burden of Regulation Commission* which I hope will take due account of David Milliband's view and that already referred to in the *Cross-Cutting Review*. I hope that at the end of the Committee's deliberations the feeling that the least threat of independent thought is treated as a subversion and a further feeling that trivialities are minutely regulated from above will disappear.

Voluntary hospices exist because of a passionate desire to provide the high standards of care which Government had failed to provide. I fervently hope that independent hospices can avoid the unremitting turbulence which successive Governments appear to impose on the NHS and which, in the complex and demanding work of caring for people at the end of life, is counter-productive, and that they can remain the oasis of calm caring which they are, subject only to proportionate regulation. If that can be achieved we will not be completely insulated from the wider world but will, I hope, continue to be a little unorthodox, a little maverick and certainly undaunted, and I am certain that we will always find more to do than is required (for which read "funded") by the State.

I cannot leave this area of discussion without a word about Charity Trustees. In his novel, 1984, Orwell, with great foresight, describes arguments about how Lottery money should be spent. Several years ago I was part of a delegation with David Praill and Jean Gafin, the Executive Director of the National Council, who met the Director of the National Lottery's Grants programme. The Lotteries Board were unaware of the voluntary nature of more than two thirds of the provision of specialist palliative care. They did not know, for example, that voluntary hospice Trustees were not paid.[2] I hope that Charity Trustees will never be paid. I was thrown out of a Latin class after one year but not before I learned that the word *charity* derives from the word *caritas* which means *love*. Being a Charity Trustee is a wonderful way of displaying that quality which is the essence at the heart of hospice care.

---

[2] Since our intervention there has been a steady flow of grants to voluntary hospices including, I am pleased to say, one to Katharine House to develop the Day Care unit and to enhance staff library facilities.

LAST LAP BEFORE THE MARATHON

"He who whispers down the well
about the goods he has to sell
will not get as many dollars
as he who climbs a hill and hollers"
(American doggerel)

By 1989, our hollering had helped us to climb the hill at the summit of which was not a million dollars, but a million pounds, which was invested in diverse ways. A watershed had been reached and we were sufficiently confident to go out to tender for the hospice building, knowing that because of the income streams which had been established, long term funding would be available for some of the proposed services. But a number of unexpected rapids still had to be negotiated.

The white water of the first rapid had originally appeared in June 1988 when a European Court of Justice ruling sent shivers down the spines of many charities including Katharine House. The ruling implied that Value Added Tax would have to be paid on the cost of the hospice building. More than 300 representations were made to the government and much publicity for our view that VAT should not be charged was generated. My own campaign included letters to the press and what some called a "spirited eleventh-hour intervention" on Channel 4's *Comment* programme which gave members of the public the chance to air their views on issues of current political argument. This was an interesting experience. The draft of my contribution was radically changed during the day I spent with the programme's editors, metamorphosing into a 'human interest' story. No matter – because in February 1989 the Prime Minister reported to The House of Commons that full advantage had been taken of the latitude inherent in the ECJ ruling to give charities a good deal. We were very grateful to the government for their interpretation and relieved at the removal of this sword of Damocles.

Incidentally, it was not at all daunting to broadcast from the seat of the Channel 4 newsreader, thanks to the effectiveness of teleprompt. It was, much to my surprise, like reading a bedtime story.

Those who collect money and give services to a charity with a specific aim, be it a building, service or a foundation are naturally anxious to see some evidence of success, so my question on BBC4 Radio Gardener's Question Time (about wild flowers in the hospice garden) was useful – not because it gave the charity nationwide publicity, but because it presaged the imminent start on the hospice building, the shell within which the kernel of care would develop.

Going out to tender and selecting a contractor had not been without its alarms. Quotations exceeded the money raised, but judicious planning and the willing co-operation of the chosen local contractor, Hinkins and Frewin, with some skilled volunteers enabled us to contrive a gradual development of the plans within available and anticipated finances, so that when Lady Ruth Dulverton (as President of the Appeal Committee) cut the first turf on 18th September 1989 in the presence of many supporters, it was clear that we would be in a position to provide the first service (a day care facility) when we moved into the hospice an anticipated 15 months later.

As long ago as 1863 Florence Nightingale in her "Notes on Hospitals" wrote "People say the effect is on the mind. It is no such thing. The effect is on the body too. Little as we know about the way in which we are affected by form, by colour, by light, we do know this, that they have a physical effect. Variety of form and brilliancy of colour in the objects presented to patients is the actual means of recovery".

This was quoted by the Kings Fund, a healthcare charity founded in the nineteenth century in a report on their twenty-first century work on "enhancing the healing environment" in which they made the point that "for many of today's patients, visitors and staff the hospital environment remains soulless, drab and depressing even though the NHS is currently in the midst of the largest building programme in history".

In the environment which we wanted to create, colour, form, space and light were all considered to be important and we were very fortunate indeed to be able to work with an architect who was able to interpret our perceptions with sensitivity and flair. His creation, which has proved to be effective and comfortable, he describes later.

A composer whose name I do not now recall once said "music is not in the notes". It can also be claimed that hospice care is not in the bricks and mortar or the furnishings and fabrics of a building, important as I have argued that these are, but rather in the practice and philosophy of the care provided.

So appointing nursing staff to commission and then run the first phase of the hospice was the final and most important, though daunting task. We just had to get it right. Our first Matron had a wealth of experience in palliative care and her commitment and dedication combined with her meticulous preparation, and above all her obvious love for the patients for whom we cared, laid the foundation of the philosophy and practice from which grew the special care for which the hospice is so valued.

WE'RE OFF

*"You matter because you are you and you matter to the end of your life.
We will do all we can not only to help you to die peacefully but also to live
until you die"*
Dame Cicely Saunders

Having been under starter's orders for just over a year it was gratifying to take
the first step of what was not really a marathon since that event is finite in
distance for everyone and in time even for the slowest participants, while we
could see no finishing line since malignant disease seems ever present and
other diagnoses began to interest us.

By the end of 1990 the hospice building was complete and almost
commissioned, the garden was taking shape and most important of all, the staff
were eager to use their skills.

Our first patient visited the Day Care hospice in February 1991. I collected
him from home and delivered him into the arms of our nursing staff. Since he
was the only referral he spent a privileged week cared for by three nurses, a
previously unheard of staff/patient ratio. Now 15 years later more than 600
patients are referred each year with more than 200 being cared for by one or
more of our services at any one time.

Development was gradual. We had taken the prudent decision to ensure that
before an additional service was introduced, it, as well as existing services,
could be funded for one year from banked funds. This we believed was
important for the stability of the service as well as for the peace of mind of
staff who had committed themselves to the organisation. It would need half a
million pounds a year to run an inpatient hospice so this was what we aimed to
achieve alongside the annual costs of day care provision.

The number of patients using day care grew and the publicity generated by the
official opening of Katharine House, a task performed by Diana Princess of
Wales in October 1991, had increased income to enable us to open the first six
beds in May 1992.

As described earlier we had been instrumental in establishing a Community
Specialist Nurse (Macmillan) service in the area and in 1994 expected that the
NHS would take over the funding of this important provision. The first cloud

on the horizon was a request for us to continue funding for a further six months then a further three. We agreed but were quite clear that we had reached our limit. We met with the Health Authority in June 1994 and were told that there was now no possibility of the National Health Service providing any funds for this service. The trick was that the responsibility for these nurses had moved to the Community Health Council, a different body with different personnel. Very neat and a good way to undermine trust and nurture cynicism. What were we to do? We did not want to lose this service which collaborated well with the Day and Inpatient care which we were offering so we capitulated and agreed to continue to fund the service on a permanent basis but on one condition, that we assumed management and thus control over the budget. Some reorganisation of our long term budgetary plans was of course necessary. The integration of hospice services, those that existed then and those that were developed later have proved that the decision was right. The two nurses moved into Katharine House in late Summer of 1994.

Four further beds were opened in 1994 and the lymphoedema clinic was established in 1995. The latter was the only development for which we did not have to take the initiative since we were approached by the Health Authority who even offered some initial pump priming funding for the purpose of establishing this facility. A third Community Nurse joined the team in 1994 and a fourth in 1995. In 2003 a Specialist Nurse was appointed to work solely in the local hospital to act as a liaison and ensure continuity of care for patients. Bereavement care predated the opening of the hospice and an education programme developed and grew with the hospice with the intention to disseminate the skills and philosophy appropriate to end-of-life care. At least one course is now provided each year for health care professionals.

Working with schools has been a feature of our activity for two years. One purpose of the work is to inform young people about the hospice and its purpose. This has resulted this year in the production of a Schools Information Brochure, written by pupils, which will, we hope, make an important and relevant contribution to our future contacts with the schools in the district. Our staff, and indeed some patients, have assisted pupils who are undertaking the Health & Social Care GCSE.

I referred earlier to the importance of the philosophy of care which permeates all we try to do in our relationship with patients and their families, and is based on what Dame Cicely Saunders asserted should be "efficient loving care".

Perhaps the best way to describe this approach is to quote from our Memorandum of Association, our Hospice Philosophy which has been developed over time and from our leaflet "A Way of Caring" which is available to patients, carers and the general public. But first for those not familiar with the term palliative care I should explain that the word *palliative* derives from Latin *pallium* meaning *a cloak*. This implies that when an illness cannot be cured, living with it can be made more comfortable as the symptoms are controlled or cloaked.

The Memorandum states that Katharine House Hospice was established "to promote the material, medical, mental and spiritual welfare of persons of either sex without regard to race or creed who are suffering from any illness that the association has been advised by a responsible body or person, is likely to terminate the life of any such person, including terminal cancer or any other terminal illness".

Our philosophy is underpinned by the World Health Organisation's definition of Palliative Care in 1990 which states that:

"Palliative Care is the active total care of patients whose disease is not responsive to curative treatment. Control of pain, of other symptoms, and of psychological, social and spiritual problems is paramount. The goal of palliative care is achievement of the best possible quality of life for patients and their families. Many aspects of palliative care are also applicable earlier in the course of the illness, in conjunction with anti-cancer treatment.

Palliative Care:

- Affirms life and regards dying as a normal process
- Neither hastens nor postpones death
- Provides relief from pain and other distressing symptoms
- Integrates the psychological and spiritual aspects of patient care
- Offers a support system to help patients live as actively as possible until death
- Offers a support system to help the family cope during the patient's illness and in their own bereavement."

We at Katharine House therefore believe that:

1. The patient has the right to the highest quality of life within realistic goals, so that s/he can be helped to "live" until s/he dies.

2. The patient can expect recognition of his/her autonomy and of his/her freedom to express where and how s/he wishes to receive care.

3. The patient can expect the appropriate involvement of his/her family in his/her care prior to death and at the point of death.

4. The patient can expect the appropriate care for members of his/her family both before and after his/her death.

5. The patient can expect to participate in decisions pertaining to his/her care, and to be cared for by staff who endeavour to work alongside him/her in order to maintain his individuality until death.

6. The patient can expect to receive professional assessment of his/her physical, emotional, social and spiritual situation, and the implementation of appropriate interventions to relieve or prevent symptoms, whilst maintaining his/her dignity.

7. The patient can expect to express and practice his/her religious, philosophical and cultural beliefs, and to express feelings and emotions related to his/her approaching death, in his/her own way.

8. The patient can expect an interdisciplinary approach which involves community staff and specialist carers, thus providing the basis for meeting his/her needs whilst enabling staff to support each other.

9. The patient can expect to receive care from competent, sensitive and knowledgeable people who respect his/her privacy, and who demonstrate an educational and research-based approach to patient care whilst fostering an environment where staff seek to update and share their knowledge.

10. The patient can expect to receive care in an environment where regular auditing of standards of care takes place, thus enabling staff to monitor and improve their practice.

11. The patient can expect that any information imparted by him/her will only be shared with those health care professionals who need to know this.

In order to achieve this philosophy Katharine House:

1. Recognises the contribution of its staff and equally of its volunteers in all departments and endeavours to support and value them, both formally through sufficient resources, clear management structures, policies, appraisals and supervision etc and informally through an atmosphere that is professional yet relaxed, one that is keen to promote a community spirit built on the uniqueness of its individual members, one that is supportive of the needs of those individuals in the pursuit of their own growth or in the crises they meet in life.

2. Recognises the unique and independent character of Katharine House as it has grown out of, and is primarily supported by, its local community, so attempts to further integrate with that community to create a strong civil society in which people do things for themselves and for each other. This is achieved by means of appropriate and varied communication of our aims and philosophy and by the recruitment of volunteers from the community into a range of roles.

3. Is clear about its roots in the national hospice movement, that developed out of a desire to witness to the fact that death and dying required a new and individual approach.

4. Endeavours to participate in all current debates in palliative care through formal and informal links with other specialist palliative care providers, and with national and local Palliative Care Associations.

5. Endeavours to co-operate and collaborate with all external bodies including Primary Health Care Teams, Social Services, Primary Care Trusts, Hospital Trusts and Networks in order to provide the best and most equitable palliative care services both now and in the future.

6. Encourages its staff not just to pursue their own development through education, but to impart their knowledge and expertise to colleagues throughout the locality both formally and informally.

7. Encourages all staff to develop a genuine sense of care that extends to all whom they meet, in an attempt to fully recognise that aspect of community to which it subscribes.

The following quotations from "A Way of Caring" will I hope complete the picture:

"We believe that our popularity and success lies in our 'way of caring'. Patients tell us repeatedly that what they want most is a simple and unrushed approach in peaceful surroundings, free from any unnecessary high-tech gadgetry, where they can relax and feel able to raise whatever issues are important to them. They appreciate being at the centre of their own care"

"Comfort, quality of life and the preservation of dignity are essential considerations"

"We put the patient at the heart of all discussions and decisions regarding their management. In conversation, we try to relate to people in ways that meet their individual needs"

"We hope that we succeed in our efforts to care and we always welcome feedback and suggestions about how we might further improve our services"

The specific needs of individuals can change over time and we have built up the experience and resources to enable us to act in flexible and personalised ways to ensure that the right parts of the service are available to those who need them when they need them.

This is our covenant with the people who turn to us for help.

HAVE WE GOT IT RIGHT?

"It's not rocket science that we are looking for just some humanity and kindness"

Quoted from 'Care of the Dying & the NHS' published by St. Christopher's Hospice, the National Council for Hospice and Specialist Care Services and the Nuffield Trust

Have we got it right? Life is a continual struggle against imperfection. One of the ways in which this struggle manifests itself in the hospice is the constant questioning by our medical and nursing staff of their actions and procedures. Reading the minutes of the various in-house committees one cannot but be impressed by the range and the detail of the issues addressed but more especially by the care and thoughtfulness devoted to the search for improved outcomes for all our patients and their relatives.

When I was a Headteacher I sometimes surprised parents by suggesting to them that I could not necessarily provide them with the "thickest cream or sweetest honey" and moreover that the perfect school that they were seeking did not exist, but rather that the one where perfection was sought did exist. I am sure that this also applies to hospices and I am certain that the struggle against imperfection is being very strongly waged here at Katharine House.

As part of the regulatory process to which we are subjected, trustees, as providers of the hospice services, are required under Healthcare Commission Regulation 26 to carry out interviews with patients twice a year to elicit their opinions about the care provided. In numerous conversations with patients over many years the overwhelming majority of opinions have been very positive. Some typical examples are quoted here:

"I can't get over the kindness"
"The degree of patience displayed by staff is amazing"
"I have 100% confidence in the staff who are caring for me"
"A feeling of security is very reassuring"
"Looking in from the outside would give no clue to the kind of care which is available; it has to be experienced"

"It is surprising to find so much love and compassion concentrated in one place"

"Nothing is too much trouble"

"I experienced a great sense of relief when I found the hospice"

"I value the feeling of security"

"I have never met such love"

"I am curious by nature and am always asking questions which are always answered fully"

"This is such a happy place. I was afraid when the hospice was first suggested but now it is the highlight of my week" (Day patient)

"The community is blessed and fortunate to have such a facility"

"I was nervous about meeting other cancer sufferers but this environment makes it easy"

"The hospice is an extension of home"

"Anyone who goes away from here with a problem does so because they haven't asked for help"

"I stepped through the door and walked into peace"

"The staff have become my friends"

Other patients and carers have written directly about their experience of Katharine House. I am grateful for their contributions which give heartfelt insights. These can be found in the Other Voices section of this book.

A third source of opinion is the many thousands of letters which have been received by our staff over the years. Permission has been granted by some of the writers to quote from them:

"What a wonderful environment you have created, we cannot praise the staff there enough, such kindness and compassion"

"I would like to take this opportunity to thank you for your most attentive and professional care that you provided for [   ] during his illness. He was always praising the level of service and commitment provided by you and on his behalf thank you for being there throughout. I would be grateful if you would pass on my sincere thanks to all the staff involved in caring for him as they were all exceptional. They showed a gentle and compassionate level of care that created a calming environment for the patients making them feel at ease in such difficult circumstances"

"During my sister's illness when she was in the care of Katharine House you may recall that we had a wide-ranging chat which I found particularly helpful in the darkness of that time, and I came to realize why [   ] had formed such profound respect for you and had such confidence in you. I would just like to take the opportunity to thank you for your compassion and kindness to her as well as your professional skilled help during these past months"

"Thank you for the care and support you gave my father during his final days at Katharine House. All the staff were so kind and professional in their work. Their approach was both personal and sensitive and we as a family were made to feel so welcome. I cannot imagine a better place in such circumstances"

"How lovely to receive your kind letter and card on my birthday telling us that we were being thought of as the anniversary of [   ] passing approached"

"The last few months of [   ] life were very sad and a dark time for all who were close to her. The one thing that does recall happier memories was her contact with Katharine House. It gave us such pleasure to see her so happy. My wife and I do want to thank you and the staff of the hospice for all your care and support during the last weeks of my sister's life. Your dedication is plain to see and we feel thankful that she was at peace in such a loving and caring environment"

"It is a great comfort knowing that you are still there and giving such a peaceful haven to all who need you"

"For years you drive past the hospice not realizing what goes on and then it becomes such an important part of your life. I cannot speak more highly of the wonderful doctors and nurses who cared for [   ] during her stay"

"I really cannot thank you enough for the love and care you lavished on [   ], and all of us, during her last days. I didn't in my wildest dreams imagine that a place like this existed, or that you could all have such a surfeit of love to share, along with the care"

"[ ]'s time in Katharine House was very short but it has left an indelible memory and bolstered my faith in human nature. It takes a special person to work in palliative care with specialist characteristics and attributes and Katharine House seems to have recruited them in abundance"

The thread woven into all of these comments is gratitude to the staff of the hospice for their skill, dedication and kindness. It has been my good fortune to witness this professionalism which has always been enhanced by a willingness to give that little extra beyond the strict call of duty.

There are many examples of this. The evening phone call to reassure a patient at home; accompanying a family on their return journey to South Africa; walking a patient's dog or taking a patient for a drive in the countryside; attending a thousand and one fundraising events; helping to arrange life-enhancing experiences at the end of a patient's life, for example journeys of various kinds, helicopter rides and even a parachute jump.

It is the day-to-day professionalism and commitment of all the staff in every department of the organisation which is at the heart of what Katharine House is able to offer and which elicits the gratitude of patients and carers alike.

Civic support has always been highly valued. Helen Gibbs and Brent Prestidge greet the fundraising cyclists
(by kind permission of the Banbury Guardian)

The original Trustees (from left to right): Dr Richard Adam, Reverend Jeff Chard, Lyn Simms, Andrew Edwards, Alan Overton, Kath Overton, Neil Gadsby (Heather Gadsby), David Stewart, Heather Stewart.
Dr Martin Harris was not present.

Dr Richard Adam "topping out" the Hospice building, August 1990

Cutting the first turf on the hospice site with Lady Ruth Dulverton who was President of the Appeal Committee

Katharine House Hospice
Two external views, a bedroom and a part of the gardens

The Princess of Wales at the formal opening of the hospice in October 1991

10 Downing Street 1992 Launch of the National Council. Later in the evening it was announced that £37 Million would be earmarked for palliative care in voluntary hospices (more than double the previous year's total)

September 2002 A conference exchange with Professor Mike Richards, the National Cancer Director

KATHARINE HOUSE HOSPICE
COST OF PROVIDING
SERVICE

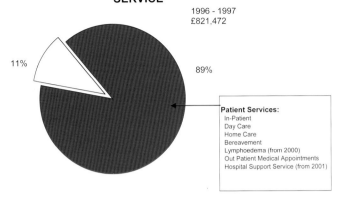

1996 - 1997
£821,472

11%

89%

Patient Services:
In-Patient
Day Care
Home Care
Bereavement
Lymphoedema (from 2000)
Out Patient Medical Appointments
Hospital Support Service (from 2001)

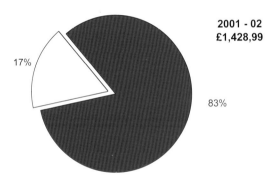

2001 - 02
£1,428,99

17%

83%

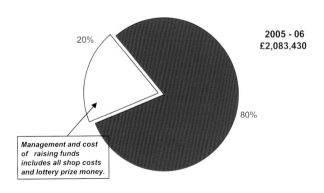

2005 - 06
£2,083,430

20%

80%

Management and cost of raising funds includes all shop costs and lottery prize money.

KATHARINE HOUSE HOSPICE
INCOME

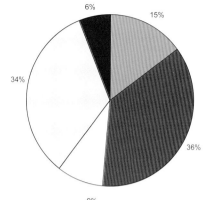

1996 - 97
£923,831

●	Sales of donated goods
◕	KHH fundraising, donations and gifts
	Legacies
	Government and other grants
●	Investments

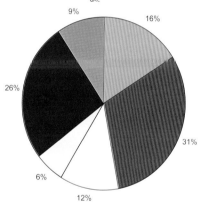

2001-02
£1,341,355

●	Sales of donated goods
◕	KHH fundraising, donations and gifts
	Lottery
	Legacies
●	Government and other grants
●	Investments

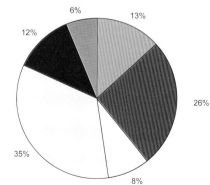

2005-06
£2,881,556

●	Sales of donated goods
●	KHH fundraising, donations and gifts
	Lottery
	Legacies
●	Government and other grants
●	Investments

FUNDING A LOCAL HOSPICE

'Health Chiefs branded mean by Hospice boss'
Headline, Banbury Guardian 1994

Frequently when surveys about a public view on charitable giving are carried out a number of issues are highlighted. The most important is the need to communicate effectively information about the charity and especially about how its money is spent.

A local charity such as a hospice is at a distinct advantage here because the longer it provides services the more local people will have direct experience of the services which their donations help to support, but since there are still those who, despite our twice yearly publications and our weekly column in the local press, believe that we are funded by the State perhaps it is appropriate to say something about our costs and the sources of our income. An indication of how income and expenditure have changed over time is shown graphically elsewhere.

The stories behind these figures are many and varied. First a word about statutory funding which includes a digression.

Is there any area of human activity which is not affected by politics? Healthcare and therefore hospice care certainly is and politics almost caused at least a torn hamstring as the starting flag went down.

In November 1990, at the Annual Conference of the National Charity *Help the Hospices*, the then Minister of State at the Department of Health had announced that the Government intended to contribute to the costs of hospice care provided by the voluntary sector. This was already happening in some localities but he wanted to achieve 50/50 funding for all voluntary hospices. In other words he wanted half of our costs to be met from statutory funds and he announced that £8 million would be made available as the first step towards that achievement. David Mellor remained my favourite politician for some time thereafter although of course his aim has not been achieved. But the Chief Nursing Officer of Oxfordshire Health Authority, with whom we had to negotiate for a share of the £8 million, almost caused the aforementioned injury since he argued, completely misunderstanding the Government's wish to support the voluntary sector, that since we had no contract with the Health Authority we did not qualify. At the end of this unnecessary skirmish we did receive £15,000 a very useful contribution to the £80,000 running costs for the first year of the Day Care Hospice.

Following this experience it seemed appropriate to seek some political advice and since local MP Tony Baldry had already been helpful in negotiating with the Department of Transport with regard to access to the site and for use of the M40 as previously described, who better to ask? He suggested that an All Party Parliamentary Hospice group of MPs who supported their own local hospice could be used to take future concerns to Government.

There are more than 300 All Party Parliamentary groups interested in a wide spectrum of human activity including sporting, commercial, scientific and leisure. It is interesting that early in 2006 The Times claimed that some of these groups were financed by industrial interest groups and were thus open to the wrong sort of influence.

The story of the founding of this particular All Party Parliamentary group is perhaps not well known. Tony Baldry suggested that I might, through my hospice contacts around the country, be able to gauge the interest of other MPs. In the event I was able to provide Tony with the names of 14 MPs who expressed an interest in joining the group. One of these was Jack, now Lord, Ashley who I met through a mutual friend and who became the group's first Chairman while Tony became its first secretary.

The All Party group needed to understand the needs of all voluntary hospices so the obvious next move was to introduce Tony and Jack to the only national body which then existed for the purpose of supporting local voluntary hospices. A meeting to brief the officers of the new parliamentary group was arranged. The meeting took place behind the Speaker's Chair and I was able to welcome Ann, Duchess of Norfolk, who had founded *Help the Hospices* in 1984 and Paul Rossi who was then Executive Director of that Charity. I understand that more than 100 MPs attended the first meeting of the group and my experience over a number of years leads me to believe that we have been able to exert influence which I think is of the right kind. I also believe that members of the group attend its meetings because they are genuinely interested in supporting their local hospice. It is interesting to note that when Hazel Blears in her former role at the Department of Health announced increased short-term funding for voluntary hospices a few years ago she did so at a meeting of the All Party group.

The average level of State funding achieved by voluntary hospices is in the region of 35% annually and that certainly applies to Katharine House in the 15 years of our existence. There are periodic increases. The Grants announced by David Mellor as described, the introduction of the internal market which gave voluntary hospices the opportunity to 'sell' their services to Health Authorities introduced by the Thatcher Government and the aforementioned injection of funding announced by the Government in 2003, which took our statutory income to 46% in that year. However, inevitably a peak of statutory funding has always been followed by a period of decline and we are currently on such a downhill slope.

The reality is that, in spite of all the initiatives over the years, the link between Government pronouncements and the local "procurers" of services (formerly Health Authorities but now the Primary Care Trusts) remains tenuous and each voluntary hospice still needs to negotiate annually for a State contribution which I reiterate has remained, over a long period of time, at just 35%. I do not think that this is a satisfactory situation for the providers of a service which makes such an important contribution to end-of-life care, an area of life to which the Government has recently made a strong commitment (see page 57).

Voluntary fundraising is really the story of a community's desire to maintain the hospice. Each time we have seen the need to introduce a new funding stream it has been well supported. Our four charity shops thrive under enthusiastic management and dedicated volunteers and contribute more than £100,000 in profit each year from donated goods. The lottery established a few years ago has 4,000 members and also contributes more than £100,000 a year to the hospice while still making 52 people a year better off by a £1,000 and many others with smaller prizes. Events run by the Appeal and Friends Committees are always financially successful and, an added bonus, enjoyable. The number of events initiated and organised by supporters is enormous and the range always fascinating from the ordinary but highly valued fetes, coffee mornings and sales through sponsored walks, beard shavings and marathons to the exotic ascents of Kilimanjaro and a heroic row across the Atlantic. I do fear that we might also have to admit some responsibility for the wearing out of the Inca Trail. A soldier marched many miles carrying a sack of coins on his back to deliver to Katharine House; a man who was admonished rather than prosecuted by the Police for a minor traffic offence "punished" himself by making a donation.

Straightforward donations, one off or regular, and a steady stream of legacies and events also contribute to the current annual income needed to provide hospice care locally. The list is continuous and endless and can be further illustrated by four people chosen at random who write in the Other Voices chapter about their own contributions, all of which, of course, to be successful, required the support of the community.

AN UNEXPECTED ROLE

"..... a packhorse in our great affairs ...."
Shakespeare

Having chosen a quotation from Shakespeare, I now realise that I have misquoted having used the wrong pronoun (a Duke was referring to a King's great affairs). However, the misquotation does seem more appropriate as a prologue to what you are about to read.

Prior to about 1990 each voluntary hospice was an isolated local organisation with no National body with which to affiliate or indeed to develop any kind of relationship. Of course, professionals could join the relevant Professional Body and an Association of Hospice Administrators (now the Association for Hospice Management) had been founded around 1980, a group which I joined as soon as I became aware of its existence.

The first opportunity to become directly involved in a National body occurred in 1989. Ann, Duchess of Norfolk, had established her National Charity *Help the Hospices* in 1984 with the aim of supporting local hospices with funds which she had proved to be adept at raising, but in 1989 *Help the Hospices* began the process which has developed over time and will shortly turn it into a membership organisation. I do not believe that the participants in the regional meetings held in 1989 perceived the vision which is now becoming a reality but the idea that advice should be sought from hospices within the regions was indeed a first step.

The Four Counties (Oxon, Bucks, Berks, Northants) meeting was held in Oxford and at the end of it I found myself, after mini-hustings with off-the-cuff speeches and a secret ballot, a member of the *Help the Hospices* advisory board which held its first meeting at the BMA in the summer of 1990.

Difficulties over the distribution of the funds earmarked by David Mellor led the Government in 1990/91 to entertain the idea of a more formal body to which it could relate and receive expert advice on matters relating to hospices and palliative care. The result was the formation of the National Council for Hospice and Specialist Palliative Care Services. This was again to have regional representation as well as representatives from some of the Professional Bodies, such as the Association for Palliative Medicine, the Royal College of Nursing Palliative Care Forum, the Association for Hospice Management and the newly formed Forum of Chairmen of Independent Hospices which I had just joined. Also involved were representatives from National bodies, *Help the Hospices*, Macmillan Cancer Support, Marie Curie Foundation and the Sue Ryder Foundation.

As a newcomer to the hospice world, (Katharine House had opened for day care in February 1991) this new organisation appeared to be necessary but of no direct concern to me. I was surprised therefore to be approached by colleagues in the region and asked to stand for election as the regional representative. Daunted but honoured I agreed and again after hustings conducted by post I was, much to my surprise, elected. It did not seem appropriate to withdraw even though I felt that the defeated candidates had greater experience than I had. Re-election three years later for a further three-year period seems to imply that my contribution had not been disastrous.

By this time I must admit that I was hugely interested in national issues which impinged on voluntary hospices so that I was pleased to be asked to join the committee of the Forum of Chairmen of Independent Hospices in 1998 and become its Chairman three years later, a role which I fulfilled until September 2003.

To complete the picture this Chairmanship involved representing the Forum on the National Council to which I returned in this new role for a further three years, and on the Independent Hospices Representative Committee a body to which I was simultaneously elected as a regional representative until I stepped down in June 2006.

What led me to take on this long term involvement with National organisations?

Whilst deeply involved in the founding of a voluntary independent hospice I had learned a great deal about the hospice movement but at the same time knew that I had much more to learn. My contacts with others in similar situations and those further along the path had convinced me that I was working informally within a movement which had many positive characteristics. After the shock of my first election it became obvious that working formally with colleagues had benefits for us all and for several years I have been carried along by a passionate belief that good end-of-life care is an important ingredient in society, and that this passion is shared by the organisations with which I have been associated.

Looking at the strategic agendas and action plans at different points in their progress one is impressed by the commonality of purpose which these organisations express. For example, *Help the Hospices* wish "to help hospices deliver high standards of care, relief and treatment of patients and support for their families and carers", and "to support the development and sustainability of independent voluntary hospices". The IHRC want "to promote the role of the voluntary sector in the development and delivery of palliative care and to champion the unique work of independent voluntary hospices" and to "ensure that IHRC's activities and priorities reflect and address the common interests and concerns of its constituents", while National Council in 2001 for example prioritised the seeking of agreement on increased funding for the voluntary sector while also working to promote good practice in palliative care and promoting the extension of palliative care to those experiencing illnesses other than cancer. While supporting all of these strategic objectives the Forum of Chairmen grew out of a recognition within the hospice movement of the increasing complexity of the job of trustees due the increasing pressure of statutory requirements.

On the printed page those statements seem formal and bland but the passion with which I have heard them discussed, always with patients and their families at the centre of the debate, is what has kept me involved for so long. Being involved with groups of people who combine social and business entrepreneurship is both stimulating and satisfying.

A few of the things with which I have been involved will give a flavour of the work but not the number, complexity and often contentiousness of the issues which have been and are still being addressed.

Organising conferences for the Forum and the National Council was a combination of privilege and hair tearing worry (speakers do cry off the day before) but presented wonderful opportunities to meet wise and compassionate people willing to share their wisdom with large audiences eager for knowledge with which to enhance their own practice. There was never a shortage of listeners to such speakers as Dr Derek Doyle whose blend of "comfort, care and rigorous scientific evidence" is at the heart of palliative care. Dr Bobbie Farsides answering but not answering the question "is there a life not worth living?" Professor Mike Richards, the National Cancer Director attempting to find a way through political and bureaucratic minefields to make palliative care more accessible. Geraldine Peacock, Chair of the Charity Commission making regulation seem amusing. Dr Carole Dacombe talking about the need to "communicate to the ill person that we care about their uniqueness".

Thring, the nineteenth century Headmaster of Uppingham, had referred to his colleagues in the rarefied world which he occupied as "a singular body of men". With the addition, of course, of "and women", I will adopt that phrase to describe my hospice chair colleagues for whom I tried to strike a balance in the Forum's activities between recognising their needs and acknowledging their many and varied skills developed during their professional lives. So commissioning Charity Trustee Networks to survey the views of Forum of Chairmen members was an activity which I found of value since it gave an insight into their needs. It was satisfying to learn that there was a high degree of satisfaction with the organisation's activities largely due I am sure to the work of my three predecessors as Chairmen. The range of topics appearing on the conference and committee agendas of all of these bodies is wide and varied but consistent. Our relationship with the Government; finance; partnerships (with other organisations and locally with the NHS); governance; definitions of palliative care and what constitutes a core service; guidance of the National Institute for Clinical Excellence; inspection by the Healthcare Commission; management issues; strategic planning; fundraising; investment; audit; hospice lotteries; legal issues recently concerning the Charities Bill. In all of these areas I have tried to argue that the independence and autonomy of a local voluntary hospice is important to the local community which supports it in a symbiotic relationship which must not be undermined.

It was particularly satisfying to have direct access to civil servants at the Department of Health and occasionally even ministers and even more satisfying when one felt that an argument had been won. For example, the former listened carefully to arguments about what at the time a few years ago were known as "the irritants". A patient referred to the NHS for care could access the whole range of services needed such as medicines, pathology services and imaging (x-ray and scan). If a patient was referred to a voluntary organisation the organisation was billed for those services. It is surprising that some health authorities got away with the practice for so long but equity has been largely achieved in this context.

Membership for a time of *Help the Hospices* Grants Committee was fascinating enabling me to see how innovative and pioneering colleagues were in the pursuit of improvements in their service. Membership as a lay man on the National Council Committee which produced guidelines on psychosocial care in palliative care and brief membership of Council's Ethics Committee confirmed my admiration for those who deal with difficult ethical decisions. Even briefer and peripheral involvement with the steering group which ultimately produced the *Help the Hospices* Guide for Hospice Trustees almost made me believe that ignorance of these matters is an underrated virtue.

One activity which I particularly enjoyed was the editorship for a number of years of the Newsletter of the Forum of Chairmen and the self appointed book reviewer of that organ. I reviewed books on governance, on management and a range of pamphlets and magazine articles relevant to Chairmen on all of the topics mentioned above but I now see that the majority of my reviews were on books of poetry all, I would claim, relevant to the hospice movement. Poetry is after all the chosen language of desire, in this case our desire to achieve the best care we can for those who turn to us.

The Independent Hospices Representative Committee was the brainchild of a group of voluntary hospice people who were dissatisfied with the National Council perceiving that it did not sufficiently address voluntary hospice issues. At the time I did not agree and made my views known. However, I did become a member of the steering group which finally established IHRC in 1999 and now admit that my initial judgement was wrong. National Council has broadened its brief, changed its name to reflect that wider brief and is unable to speak unequivocally with a voluntary hospice voice which is now so vital, and without IHRC it is doubtful that the proposed membership organisation could have developed. From my position now on the sidelines I would urge the new organisation which will be the UK Hospice Committee legally linked to *Help the Hospices* when it finally fledges in 2007 to do nothing which undermines the independence of local voluntary hospices.

Sixteen years ago when meeting representatives of the local health authorities in the region to explain the purpose of the new National Council one quickly realised that end-of-life care was not necessarily a high priority. Now in 2006 the Government has announced its intention to develop a comprehensive strategy for end-of-life care and the setting up of a ministerial Board to pursue this objective. This is a welcome development and probably a tribute to the efforts of the organisations sketchily described here. Commenting on the plan at the All Party Parliamentary Group in June 2006 Professor Mike Richards commented "this strategy will not be a quick fix this will be a strategy for the long term". I hope it will not take another sixteen years and will be ready in time for my demise.

Of course, for a particular group of patients, those cared for by voluntary hospices, it is already in place. Currently (early 2007) the Parliamentary Public Administration Select Committee is discussing contestability (it used to be called competition). The Committee will be asking whether charities are as effective as the State in providing public services and considering whether small organisations are equipped to take on some of the work. I hope that the Committee will look at the 189 voluntary hospices and learn from these organisations which did not need to contest with the State. They just got on with the job.

I do not recall who said or when that "the proper duty of the philanthropist is to force society to do its duty" but I do know that it was Lord Shaftesbury in 1883 who argued that "State bureaucracy is a melancholy system that tends to debase a large number of people to the condition of a nursery where the children look to father and mother and do nothing for themselves". Voluntary hospices have never enrolled in the nursery. They are not perfect, show me a human institution that is, but are a rich leavening in society. They need only two things from the State. First, the more realistic contribution to their costs, which has so often been promised but has not yet materialised (although readers will not be surprised that I would view full-cost recovery with disquiet). In every voluntary hospice the present was once a future ambition reached because of a desire to improve end-of-life care and the courage to pursue ideals. The present is widely acknowledged to be good and there is no danger that we will compromise our achievements by relaxing our endeavours, so the second requirement is the trust which would be implicit in the lightest of regulatory regimes.

OTHER VOICES

"What matters is what we do for each other"
Lewis Carroll

The first part of this book written by one of the participants in the Katharine House story is, I am sure, partial and fragmentary. However, the story is made up of a huge mosaic of voices and activities and a small sample of the owners of those voices have been persuaded to contribute to balance the perhaps too personal perspective from which I have viewed events.

Some are users of the hospice services who by sharing their experiences with us show a courage, determination and wisdom from which we can all benefit; some are contributors in a range of ways and others are both users and contributors. They represent a tiny part of the enormous community activity which has made Katharine House what it is today.

Derek Kerrison

"I've just looked in the dictionary at the definition of the word *oasis*. It says 'An oasis is a small area in the desert where water and plants are found'. For me and so many, Katharine House is an oasis of love and very special care.

Many years ago when Dorothy, my late wife, and I came from London to live in Adderbury, we had no idea that one day such a wonderful facility would be developed so close to our home. In fact, Katharine House Hospice became Dorothy's home for just a short time before departing to another dimension. Just a short while ago, I found one of Dorothy's notebooks (she had many) in which she had listed the names and shift rota of the nurses and medical staff who looked after her. As always, the notes were half written in shorthand and the remainder in long-hand. So be it.

A highlight for Dorothy was helping to prepare some of the paperwork prior to the visit by Princess Diana. At the last minute, it was discovered that a good quality pen was required for Diana to sign the visitor's book or some other documents. Never to fail, Dorothy loaned a gold pen and pencil set which had never been out of its box. Unfortunately the price tag had not been removed. Trust Diana to turn this situation into one of her inimitable smiles.

It was because of Dorothy's long-standing contact with Katharine House as a volunteer on the administration side that I became involved. My contribution is best described as a casual volunteer. When the bugle sounded I responded. I can't recall all the various tasks, so suffice to note a few highlights:

- Sorting postage stamps into specified groupings was an onerous and time-consuming task. Our dining table (extended) often became a stamp sorting bench. No one was allowed to go to bed until all the foreign stamps had been sorted from the Brits – true discrimination.
- Another task was to stuff envelopes with the Annual Report and other items of print. After completing the first thousand envelopes when you looked at the pile remaining, it appeared greater than when you started. In those days, two other volunteers, Vikki and Agnes, were around to make sure everyone followed the master plan. These two gallant ladies master-minded the production of re-cycled greeting cards – they did a wonderful job.
- Another of my contributions has been holding a collection box outside supermarkets and other hot-spots. What a wonderful experience. Apart from the generous financial response it is vitally important to keep the image of Katharine House in front of the local community. Not that most need reminding. Many of the people, young and old, who respond to the collection box relate past memories of loved ones who underwent care at the Hospice. They all have words of sincere gratitude.
- The most recent task I became involved in was a job in the kitchen making lunchtime sandwiches for members of staff. The full-time kitchen staff, working under Ann, move around so fast you can hardly see them. I call it The Katharine House Commonwealth Kitchen Games.

During these notes I purposely avoided making any mention of the names of the medical team who looked after my wife Dorothy. They know I recognise and appreciate all the kindness and care they extended to her.

The Chinese have a saying *No loss, no gain.* It was so sad that the Chairman of the Hospice, Neil Gadsby, and his wife suffered the sad loss of their daughter, Katharine, at such an early age. One thing is certain, Katharine always will be observing the establishment and growth of Katharine House."

"After passing the shady willow trees there will be
bright flowers and another village ahead"
Master Li Hongzhi – Falun Gong

Joyce and Den Whitmarsh

Katharine House – what it has meant for me, a carer of my wife of nearly 53 years who is suffering from P.S.P. (Progressive Supranuclear Palsy) and is in her fifth year since being diagnosed with the disease. We have sold our house near Bath and come to live with our daughter Lisa and her family at an extension to their house in a purpose-built ground-floor flat in the village of Marsh Gibbon.

Having had a P.E.G. feeding system fitted at the Radcliffe Infirmary, Oxford, our doctor thought that what was needed was a little T.L.C. from carers with a nursing background and how right he was. Joyce was admitted soon after for a week's stay at the end of which she was offered a further week's respite in three months time but was also asked if she would like to attend for a few hours each Wednesday. Having lost her sense of balance, unable to speak coherently, unable to see properly and having difficulty swallowing meant that both of us were quite apprehensive.

Wednesday morning came around and off we went the 14 miles to Adderbury. We were greeted by a group of smiling people who offered us coffee and, after getting Joyce's lunch organised, I was gently eased out of the door and I was told that they would expect me at around 3.30 pm. I returned and was greeted with a big smile from Joyce and when asked how she had got on, a further big smile and a big thumbs up. The same response I had to each question – like, did you enjoy lunch, etc. I then found out that she had joined an art class. I could not believe my ears, bearing in mind that Joyce's signature was neither in a straight line nor legible as it had been until her early seventies. The next week, the 'mistress piece' I was allowed to see. I was 'gob-smacked' and truly delighted but was assured by those present that Joy had 'done the painting'. This has given her a new lease of life, so much so that each member of our immediate family was given a 'mistress piece' as part of their Christmas present, 15 paintings in all! The one painting we have retained however was the very first one, that of a poppy, which I treasure. This has given Joyce a new lease of life and I thank all the staff at Katharine House for their help and making our lives that much richer.

John Crook

Life in the hospice:
First, from the medical point of view, it is comforting that there is someone on call with a range of options, day and night (and weekends), which would not be available at home.

Secondly, the ability to have visitors day or night is much appreciated and the opportunity to have a spouse stay overnight in the hospice, or even in the same room is quite remarkable.

Certainly, this particular hospice seems to go out of its way to provide for a patient's wishes to make them more comfortable. Its ready acceptance of alternative methodology is yet another example of this hospice's care. I have got a great deal out of massage sessions and reiki and have also learned to relax, with the aid of the hospice-provided counsellor.

The food in general has seemed like home-cooking and nothing seems too much trouble. I really feel that such facilities should be available in every village-sized community in the country; an improbable wish but something worth saying.

Celia Crook

Staying in the hospice:

Over the last few weeks of my husband's stay here I have found so much strength from the support of all the staff. Whenever I have been feeling low or upset there has always been someone there to listen, comfort and provide helpful words. I feel as though I am amongst friends.

This time hasn't been one full of tears, we have been able to have plenty of happiness and laughter. It has been wonderful to make John's room into a little extension of our home (often very untidy!). Visitors have been able to come and go as they please, and been made to feel welcome, never pushed out. My grown-up children have been able to stay here so that they can benefit from the short time we have left together.

John has been treated with utter kindness and consideration, his feelings and wants always come first. I have witnessed his anxiety flow away from him under the calming influence of those caring for him.

I cannot begin to imagine what these weeks would have been like if he had been at home or in hospital. Instead of a nightmare, this has been a time for us to grow together, show our love and have happy memories.

John King

During October 2002, following a severe internal bleed, I was admitted to the John Radcliffe hospital and subsequently diagnosed as having prostate cancer. This was a very traumatic time for me and my wife because on May 14 2001, our son had died from this same disease after suffering four years of intense pain. The day after my diagnosis, I was transferred to the Churchill hospital where I received radiotherapy and after a week I came home. I was very weak and in low spirits. I had also developed complications with bowel problems and diabetes. Although I had been diabetic for some years my usual tablets were not controlling blood sugar levels because I was taking steroids for the cancer so I was put on insulin injections. During the next few weeks my complications became more severe and my GP suggested to my wife that he was thinking of trying to get me admitted to Katharine House Hospice. I cried and pleaded with my wife not to let me go as I thought people only went there to die. How wrong I was!

Eventually I agreed to go and stayed for three weeks. I was discharged on 20 December just in time for Christmas. The treatment I received in the ward was absolutely superb with all the staff totally dedicated to the care and wellbeing of their patients, so gradually my complications were controlled and I was feeling better. I am certain that my life was saved by these wonderful nurses. Early in 2003 I was asked if I would like to attend the Day Unit and made my first visit on January 15. I have attended almost every Wednesday since. For the first four months I was a wheelchair patient and required a bath each week as I was unable to use the facilities at home. Eventually I was able to walk again with a walking aid after a tremendous amount of help from physiotherapists and I was put back onto tablets to control my blood sugar levels.

The volunteer drivers who transport patients to and from the Day Unit are excellent as are all the other volunteer workers. Their aim is to give patients all the help and care which they require and they are all dedicated to that purpose. I find my visits to the Day Unit to be very therapeutic and it is very nice to converse with other patients who can just sit and read, make jigsaw puzzles, solve crosswords or like myself, do something artistic in the very well supplied Art Room.

As with all other areas of Katharine House, the nurses on duty in the Day Unit are so good and are completely dedicated to the welfare of their patients. I cannot finish without mentioning the high standard of the food which the nurses and volunteers help to serve.

Zoe Mills

The Katharine House Hospice is a wonderful, purpose-built, building set in lovely grounds. There is such a lovely calm peaceful atmosphere in the ward. The patients are very well looked after by the nurses and doctors – nothing is too much trouble for them. In the Day Centre artwork is an option – some paint pictures, or like my husband, learn decoupage. He made two trays which

I have still got. He also painted a kingfisher on glass which hangs in the window. There is a chapel where services are held every Thursday for in-patients and out-patients and anyone else who might be interested, such as staff or volunteers. The patients take part by reading the Bible. The chaplain is also very good – kind and helpful.

My husband was an out-patient at first, but was an in-patient for the last few weeks. Patients not only come from Banbury and the surrounding villages, but from much further away. There is a guest room upstairs which is en-suite and has drink-making facilities – I stayed in this the last few nights. Also I was with Jim during the day during which time I was given all meals for which I was not charged nor were the patients – so I regularly fed the collecting box in reception to show my appreciation. Most of the finances are from voluntary contributions.

The Hospice came to mean such a lot to me over the time Jim was there – I felt I wanted to repay them in some way so I became a volunteer. I had to wait two years before this happened. I believe there are over three hundred volunteers who work in various departments - the garden, reception, the ward and in the offices upstairs where I work (lottery, finance and administration). I do filing, photocopying, shredding and ripping, getting rid of old archives and anything else. There are about four or five who work in the card department where they re-vamp old Christmas cards and others and sell them in aid of the Hospice – another form of income. Again upstairs there is a lovely atmosphere, so you can see what Katharine House means to me.

Patricia Sones

I have had breast cancer since nearly four years ago. I was dismayed beyond belief to find I had breast cancer and I had no idea what was in store for me. It was pretty damn scary.

I had to come to Katharine House first because I had a double mastectomy and I had a lymphoedema, so I had to see the lymphoedema nurse. The thing that scared me most, wasn't that I had to go to have surgery, or that I had a double mastectomy, or chemotherapy …… it was that I had a Macmillan Nurse! This was the most scary thing because my attitude was, Macmillan Nurses look after the dying. I didn't feel a bit like I was ready to do anything like that even though I'd been told I had cancer. So I had to swallow hard and come up here. I'd always supported the shop in Banbury because I thought it was brilliant …. but it wasn't for me, it was for people dying, right? So to come through that front door was one of the most scary things I ever did. I came in and met the Macmillan Nurse and had my arms measured and took off like a jack rabbit!! I felt I wasn't having that. I felt I'd been put in the starting blocks for the last furlong stakes and I wasn't having that.

I did a lot of things that traditional medicine wouldn't approve of like alternative medicines, which cost me a fortune … went to different clinics for two, three and four weeks at a time and I became extraordinarily healthy, but I still had cancer! And eventually I did have to have a double mastectomy.

In the last year/six months I have now found that the cancer has moved to my bones, hips and spine. Things are moving on and I've got to readjust from 'just having breast cancer' to more or less mobility and a specialist nurse, who I hadn't seen for a year, or probably longer, came round again. I was having radiotherapy and she was helping with the drugs that help relieve physical discomfort and she suggested that maybe I would like to come to Katharine House and come to the Art Class.

I thought, well here we go, she's manoeuvring me into here! I was like a very unhappy filly trying to avoid the situation but the art class sounded too good to be true and reluctantly agreed to her offer to come and see the wonderful art room. It is fabulous – I wouldn't miss it for the world. It is my third week and if I had to go anywhere else today, I wouldn't have been well enough.

It is difficult to explain what made that change. At sixty seven I suppose I have to accept that I'm now mixing with seventy, eighty, ninety year olds – the ones I used to look after as a carer. It is a bit odd joining rather than being a carer, but that doesn't matter, we have so much in common. For example, we can talk about the medication like the steroids and how they affect you, make your face change shape. They've all been through it too and it is quite comforting. One person told me how 'last year, they didn't think I'd make it for another two weeks and here I am'. So that's a brilliant story! He told me how he came in dying and then went home practically alright and so I realised people don't just die here.

Now I feel I'm living a golden life. It is such a privilege actually. If you are going to die of something, the Big C is one of the better ways simply because you are the elite here. All these facilities. Suffering from an old age complaint, with no glamour to it, I know many old ladies who just sit in a tiny flat, in their bedroom. If they are lucky, they visit an old people's club, but that is nothing compared to all we are offered here. But with cancer, you have this facility here which is top five star. It is very easy for people to say 'be positive' but how can you be if you don't have such a facility to make that possible?

I have three sons who enable me to do things. Go round the world, make a film, give me a computer so I can edit it. None of which I could be positive about without the opportunity. I have a talent to paint. It has been sadly neglected. To be able to come here and develop it, have a really good lunch, not have to go home and cook, to feel good…. To have another one of your lights shining, I think that's a way of putting it. Different parts of your person to be developed in different ways. Other people are writing about their memories and what a wonderful way to validate their lives. They can feel they have described their life story and it has not died with them, just like I am editing my video, taped as a validation of me.

Now I have another project. I have spent thirty five years looking at the work-life balance and I want to put it on the computer here, and then through my website, start a discussion forum. I'm working on it on the computer. To be given a centre, a focal point to do that from, rather than trying to do it alone at home, is such a fantastic facility.

The nicest thing I have seen is to see the carers coming in to collect their relative and having had a break (having been a carer myself, to have a break and do what you want to do is so important). A break like this keeps the cost down and helps the carer not to wear out (if the caring gets too much, they back-off and feel guilty). Supported, then, the last stage isn't so frightening … dying isn't a problem but how you die is very, very important. Birth and death are two sides of the same coin. There is nothing wrong with dying, the infamous side is dying in loneliness, grief and rejection. I think the hospice system, and this hospice in particular, is the way to go.

Jackie

I have been coming to the hospice since December 2005. It has really helped me. I have met some lovely people and I have also started making cards, which I didn't know I could do. And after I've had a day at the hospice, I must say I am so relaxed. Everybody is so friendly. The food is out of this world. That's why we put on the pounds. As for the nurses and volunteers, I just can't say enough about them … there's always someone there to listen to you and what you say doesn't go around; that matters a lot. It means a great deal coming here.

Talking with John Jack

"Why do you come to the hospice?"

"For the companions … to come and see my friends…like John here (volunteer). Do you remember - I met him on the ward? I should like to see him again. I know where he lived but I don't know what Nursing Home he went to…"

"You hadn't met him before coming here? What, you spent a week together?"

"Yes"

"So that was nice.."

"Yes, he were a farmer and I were a farm worker… still that ain't about it, is it…"

"Oh, yes!"

"Well, I wouldn't have met any of these if I hadn't have come here. I should like to come and stay again but they told me, not till the middle of February, you're booked up or something…"

"So you look forward to coming in?"

"I do, yes. And my sister is glad to get rid of me! For a day…"

"It gives her a break"

"I've just met the doctor and told him off again. I met him in Banbury hospital in two different wards!!"

"So that's nice - when you go to the big hospital, you meet the same doctors. It makes it more friendly."

"Yes, 'cause I don't know anyone up there or on the wards there."

"What do you like about it here, apart from the fish in the pond. I know you like the fish!"

"Well, it's the companionship and it's quiet. I should like to be here more times. I'd like to come several times a week. What am I doing at home? Nothing!"

"So before you had a very active life and then you had to sit at home, did you?"

"I was doing my job beating at Hook Norton, as it happens. Mr. Hugh's. I was walking round with this lady and I was learning her what to do, and all at once, instead of walking with her, I was looking up at her. She said 'You're going straight to hospital'. She was a doctor and I was trying to learn her…   I've got an electric buggy but I can't go out, unless there's someone with me… like on Saturday night, I don't know what happened. Like in here, as you've seen… it happens quick."

"So coming here makes all the difference then?" "Ah, that it does".

Ray Charman

I write this memoir at a painful time in my life. My mother, who is eighty six, fell at home three months ago and remains in hospital. My two brothers and I no longer recognize the mum we have known and loved all our lives. We hope she does recover but we fear she has lost the will to live.

Two years ago my father died in hospital. Another case of "the operation was successful but the patient unfortunately died". He did not die with dignity and was miserable and in mental anguish for the last few weeks of his life.

Why do I mention these experiences? Well, because as we all know and appreciate, the experience of patients, relatives and carers at Katharine House is so different.

When my wife Jan entered the last phase of her battle against malignant melanoma in the autumn of 1992, I had worked in the health service for thirty years. I was a Chief Executive who had done just about every type of management and administrative job in the NHS. I had the best possible training, including being fortunate enough to be one of the lucky forty or so on the two year graduate national training scheme. As such, I had actually worked in every department and specialty and with every type and grade of staff in the NHS. But that autumn in 1992, I had never stepped a foot inside a hospice.

I have to say what I found made me feel amazingly grateful. My worries and fears and hopes were shared with and by everyone there – patients and staff. Although I was incredibly sad for Jan and our family and friends, and often out of my mind with grief, I felt we were safe; in good, caring, professional hands. We were also very lucky because Katharine House had not been open for long; indeed we may have been amongst the first to use a family room. My memories are, of course, jumbled and could well be inaccurate but some things, of course, burn indelibly into one's mind. Here goes with my highlights, for today at least:

- Walking in the sun in the garden pushing Jan in a wheelchair; Jan was a very keen gardener and we went into the garden whenever we could.
- Listening to a concert in the lobby; a group of ladies played Pachelbel's 'Canon in D' whilst tears streamed down our faces.
- A group hug with some staff and Jan's parents because her father wasn't able to express his emotions easily.

- Cooking breakfast in the kitchen in the early hours because we had a sudden craving.
- Writing and reading in Jan's room in an attempt to keep up with some of my work.
- Waking in the night to see a nurse on her knees sobbing quietly whilst holding Jan's hand.
- Carol singing at Christmas with joy and gusto.
- A group of Jan's friends sitting on the floor around the bed while she told them stories.
- Being called to be with Jan when I was taking a shower in the staff quarters.
- Being asked (rather frequently, as I recall) if I wanted a whisky before bed.
- Bleak cold winter days for taking a breath of air then to return to warm, cosy Katharine House for hot chocolate.
- A nurse persuading me that it was probably good for both Jan and I to share a bed some nights.

I have left out so many other similar moments but they too would have in common the fact that none of these could or would occur in a hospital. The focus is different there and they can all too easily seem complicated, faceless institutions lacking the personal, homely touch of the best hospices such as Katharine House. I am sure we would all want the opportunity to be cared for like Jan was rather than like my parents have been. I was grateful and overwhelmed by admiration for everyone who works there, and I always will be.

Roger, (Catherine & Richard) Worrall

In March 1990 my wife, Carol, gave birth to our daughter Catherine thus completing our family with my son Richard who had been born in 1984.

The following month, after being a member for seven years of Banbury Cross Round Table, I was elected their Chairman. Throughout my membership of Round Table, I had always particularly enjoyed the fundraising and community service activities. Later that year, Round Table became aware that the new Katharine House Hospice was now open to day patients, that the wards were nearing completion and that they were still trying to raise funds to complete the building. I contacted the Reverend Jeff Chard, a trustee of the Hospice, to organise a visit for Round Table. A few weeks later, we duly arrived at the Hospice and were shown around the facilities by Jeff. All of the Tablers were extremely impressed with the building's layout, its facilities and also the beautiful setting.

Looking back now, I clearly remember a comment that Jeff made in the art room that evening. He said "Many of the patients who come into this room initially believe that they do not possess any drawing or painting skills, but we find that the majority of these patients have latent skills that they are able to develop". Little did I realise the significance of this comment. Round Table duly made a donation to the Hospice in my year as Chairman.

In 1992, I retired from Round Table having reached the then maximum age rule of 40. I was then very lucky to have been invited to join the Rotary Club of Banbury, joining many of my former colleagues from Round Table. I quickly found that the Rotary Club of Banbury, with over seventy members, was extremely active both in fundraising, community service and international aid. One of their particular favourite charities, that they supported every year, was the Hospice. Every Christmas Rotarians stand outside two local supermarkets over two weekends, hand-winding a barrel organ and collecting donations from shoppers. We are always pleasantly surprised at the generosity of the shoppers. It is extremely easy to collect when your named charity is Katharine House, so many people have a connection with the Hospice.

I will now skip to 1998. Carol had a minor operation to remove a very small growth at the base of her spine. This was followed by another operation approximately a year later and yet another a year later.

In April 2001, Carol again went into the Hospital with another growth and overnight she became unable to walk and incontinent. She was diagnosed some four weeks later as having a maxillary ependyoma and we were totally astounded to be told that this was a terminal illness, that she was only expected to live another three months and would require immediate palliative care.

We converted the dining room into a makeshift bedroom and brought Carol home from the hospital. The next few weeks were extremely hard for Carol and myself adjusting to the reality of what was happening. Our family General Practitioner arranged for Carol to spend a couple of days per week at the local hospital rehabilitation centre. Unfortunately Carol did not enjoy this; the other patients were elderly persons recovering from strokes, etc. A few weeks later we received a telephone call from a specialist nurse at the Hospice who arranged to visit us. Whilst the nurse was with us, she tried to persuade Carol to attend the Hospice for a few days per week, but following her then recent experience at the hospital day centre, Carol was extremely reluctant. Eventually she did agree to let me take her for one day the following week. I duly took Carol to the Hospice and later that day, I asked her how her day had been. She had enjoyed herself, meeting other patients and particularly commented on the friendly nurses and the relaxed atmosphere, lovely building and wonderful food. At home, Carol was having to put up with my cooking!

Over the next three years, Carol underwent a course of chemotherapy, a number of radiotherapy treatments, together with minor operations. The chemotherapy course was debilitating and made Carol very ill. Over a period of six months, she lost three stone in weight and some of her hair. Throughout this time, her attendance at the Hospice kept her spirits up and her determination to survive. If for any reason Carol could not attend the Hospice for a few days she became a little depressed and concerned about not knowing how the other patients were. Carol spent a lot of her time at the Hospice in the Art room. Throughout her life she had enjoyed embroidery, etc., but had never been an artist. With the encouragement of the Art teacher, she suddenly started to produce wonderful water-colour pictures and silk paintings.

Despite being told that she would not walk again, Carol was determined to prove the doctors wrong and within six months of being diagnosed, she was walking confidently with a zimmer frame. A few months later, she was managing to climb the stairs to our bedroom. One day, we attended an appointment at Oxford with the oncologist who had told her that she would not walk again. Carol walked into the consulting room using her zimmer frame and was very annoyed to find the oncologist had been called away. One evening when I came home, Carol told me that she was going on holiday next week to the Hospice to give me a break from caring for her. She really enjoyed her "holiday" and the children and myself visited her every day.

Over the last few months of her life, Carol's symptoms worsened and she was on oxygen a lot of the time. Despite her failing health, she was nearly always full of spirit, fun and concern for our children and the other patients at the Hospice. In May 2004, she became very ill and was admitted to the Churchill Hospital in Oxford. After a few days, they told us that she did not have very much time left. Carol asked that I contact the Hospice and ask that she be transferred there as soon as possible as she wished to be in familiar surroundings with her family and friends (the staff). I spoke to the Hospice and Carol was transferred by midday, where upon arrival at the Hospice, she became very relaxed. The next day, she asked to see Maurice Humphris, a family friend, to arrange her funeral. Maurice came along later that day when Carol asked him for "Another one bites the dust" by Queen and a pink coffin. I do not think Maurice initially realised that Carol was joking with him; her sense of humour was still with her.

Myself, our children and our very good friends, Nancy Haynes, Pauline and Charles Swain, spent the next two days and nights with Carol until she sadly passed away. We were also joined by family and friends, Patricia and Peter Fowler and Jan and Jonathan Lea, who were a great support to us. All the time we were at the Hospice, the staff were continually concerned as to our well-being. We became used to them telling us that there was a meal on the table. If we had been asked if we would like a meal, we would probably have said no, not wishing to trouble anyone.

Carol passed away peacefully on the second evening with family and friends close by. I rang her brother, Brian, in Australia to tell him the sad news only to find that he was already on his way to see her. Brian arrived next morning

Hospice nurse Karen very kindly agreed to speak at the funeral. She reminded us of Carol's unique sense of humour as she was always apparently making the staff and other patients laugh and cheer up. I do not know how Carol, myself and our children, Richard and Catherine, could ever have managed to live through the three years without the dedicated caring love and support of everyone at Katharine House Hospice. We will be for ever grateful and hold this very special place and staff in our hearts and thoughts for the rest of our lives.

A Bereavement Volunteer – June Smith

The Katharine House Hospice Bereavement Service was launched on June 28th 1989 before the Hospice was even built and I was one of the original team of twenty volunteers. We had a rigorous training of one weekend a month for thirteen months under expert guidance, which included experiential work on our own personal development, learning about the grief process and the principles of counselling with many role-play situations.

I had surprised myself in being selected for the Bereavement Team. Previously I had very much wanted to train as a School Counsellor and had been unable to obtain a secondment within my profession of Teaching. Then, in 1988, I spotted the Banbury Guardian notice giving details of a seminar on Death and

Loss to encourage recruits for Bereavement Counselling for the new Hospice project. The seminar was a real eye-opener for me shedding much light on the life losses I had experienced and explaining how by understanding and acknowledging loss in life and accepting death can assist us to live more positively in the Now – that, in effect, life and death are linked. Then I knew that this was something I wanted to do.

That original team had its first base in a small suite of rooms over the old Hospice shop in North Bar, Banbury, and we took referrals from local GPs in the community and later from the Macmillan Nurses. Now, seventeen years on, we have an office base at the Hospice and Bereavement support is an essential part of the service, offered free, by the Hospice. Most of the referrals today come via the hospice, but can still be done through GPs or be self-referral. We usually have a Team strength of sixteen plus, with each volunteer having an average case-load of five or six clients with regular recruiting every two-to-three years.

I have worked under several Supervisors and seen many volunteers come and go in the Team, but still, after seventeen years, I get a lot of rewards from the work. Sometimes people comment to me that bereavement work must be morbid, but I have always found it to be positive, hopeful and with many rewards. It is a great privilege to be allowed to share the feelings and the pain of people, probably at their lowest ebb in life. We listen to their story, help them to understand the natural process of grieving and later help them to see the progress they are making in rebuilding and adjusting to a different life for themselves. Our purpose is to be a steady 'rock' and to support them through their darkest days and share the experience with them. The reward comes in seeing a client move out of the dark place and into the light once again. Sometimes we are able to see them take up new ways of life and interests and even new partners and at other times we help clients to accept where they are and to find a place for their grief.

I certainly know that this work has taught me a great deal over the years. It has helped me to grow in love and compassion as a person; to be more pro-active about living my life to the full and to accept death as merely a natural conclusion to life. Recently, in one of our training sessions, the current Bereavement Team recorded a CD of a song we had composed together, describing our work. It is called 'A Road Together' and the following reprise from it, I think, sums up what we do.

"It's a road together that we share
Side by side, but we don't know where.
It's a road together – we're moving on
Like a river flowing, flowing strong.
………
The reflection in the window
May never be the same
Endings make beginnings
We can share the pain."

A founder Trustee – Dr. Richard Adam

In 1984, I had been working for thirteen years as one of three Consultant General Physicians at the Horton General Hospital. Between us, supported by a small junior medical staff, we were responsible for the care of all emergency adult medical patients admitted to the hospital and for providing some specialist medical services throughout the day and night. The provision of specialist services in respiratory medicine brought me in contact with many patients suffering from lung cancer and other potentially fatal illnesses. Since 1981, I had the opportunity to undertake the hospital care of a few terminally ill private patients in rather better conditions than were possible within the NHS; there was more staff, the physical conditions were better, with more privacy, and I could devote more time. The degree of improvement was disturbing.

Jeff Chard was then one of a team of Church of England priests based in Banbury. On 14th September 1984, he and Stella Fairbairn, on behalf of the voluntary organisation CRUSE (also involved in the care of the terminally ill and bereaved) wrote to a number of people in local charities, working in the local hospital and in general medical practice, hosting a meeting to explore whether it could be possible to provide some day centre support for the terminally ill. Seven of us met at St. Mary's Centre on 25th October. We all knew there was a problem; perhaps we all saw it from different perspectives, but it was so revealing to hear other accounts and to realise our ignorance. We did not even know how many people in total, quite apart from how many had poor symptom control, or mobility problems, or could benefit from help from a social worker, or had religious problems, financial problems, need of a bath, help from a solicitor, help for their relations – to mention but a few. How were we to discover? More importantly, how could we learn from others who had done this? I undertook the, relatively, very simple task of finding out how many patients with cancer there were. Needless to say, my secretary did all the endless phone calls but she was immediately enthusiastic of the project.

At our second meeting on 29th November, we learned of the existence of the *Katharine House Hospice* group. We clearly needed to meet them. [I remember that dark winter's night in the back seat of Jeff's car, searching the unfamiliar country roads.] We were obviously sympathetic and synergistic. They established a Charitable Trust on 21st January 1985 and on 2nd May 1985, Jeff Chard and I joined them as Trustees.

I can confirm Neil's description of the extent of our ignorance. I realised that I needed some more formal training in Palliative Care. I was so fortunate to be awarded one of the Medical Fellowships awarded by the charity *Help the Hospices* and spent a month at Ty Olwen Hospice in Swansea in November 1986. This was invaluable, and I was particularly grateful to the very open hospitality of all the staff and their ability to discuss the problems of organisation, finance, building design, staffing, relations to more traditional care and to "alternative" care. Their Home Care Sisters [Macmillan Nurses] took great care to show me how their service functioned, much of it in remote parts of the "Valleys".

A palliative care service was a much larger project than I had appreciated.

Note: Richard has been far too modest. He was admitted to the Register of Palliative Care Physicians and became the first, and much respected, Medical Director of Katharine House – a role which he fulfilled on a voluntary basis for nine years. An impressive and highly valued contribution.

A General Practitioner – Dr Richard Lehman

I came to Banbury in 1979, a young GP, joining a small practice run by Veronica Fisher from the ground floor of a Victorian house. I wanted to see the practice grow, and to learn all the hands-on skills of general practice, including what was then known as 'terminal care'. The hospice movement had by then made everyone aware of the deficiencies of end-of-life care in hospital, but it did not yet have the resources to address the problem. The answer – at least for the time being – seemed to lie in improving care at home. Since there were as yet only a handful of Macmillan nurses in the whole of England, this meant improving my own skills, working alongside district nurses who were then, as now, the unsung heroines of the NHS. They provided me with wonderful examples of practical compassion and a wealth of experience and expertise, but I was still often aware of the shortcomings of my own medical knowledge in looking after patients with advanced cancer.

The coming of Robert Twycross as a visiting consultant in what was still called 'terminal care' gave me a chance to remedy that. Not only could one accompany him to visit patients at home, but one could also, I learnt, invite oneself to trail him on the wards at Sir Michael Sobell House, then the only hospice in Oxfordshire. This was a formative experience. From then on, I have seen palliative care as the model of good medical practice in all spheres – close attention to the patient's story, careful assessment of needs, both medical and non-medical, a clear plan to address them, and meticulous attention to detail in achieving symptom control and in monitoring progress. If only we could come up to the mark all of the time! That was the challenge Robert set us.

When I heard that there were moves afoot to create a hospice for North Oxfordshire, I was naturally keen to be involved, though regretful then, as now, that it had to be funded by voluntary donations rather than the NHS. But what a magnificent achievement it has been for all those who devoted their time, energy and money to create it from nothing! And who have kept it going so devotedly, ever since. I was a tiny bit-player in the early days – I can remember attending a planning meeting in the mid-1980s at the home of a fellow GP, Martin Harris, and visiting a hospice in York with Richard Adam. I was happy to put my name down for the on-call rota, should it ever be built.

A year or two later, my father, who was in his mid-70s and had had a heart attack, began to develop signs of heart failure. His distressing intermittent progression towards death made me aware that it is not only cancer patients who need good palliative care. I had tried to put in place the necessary arrangements for him to die peacefully at home when a further blow came – my mother became very ill and turned out to have advanced ovarian cancer. My father did indeed die peacefully at home, but in looking after my mother for the final months of her life, I was immeasurably grateful for specialist palliative care services, and above all for Katharine House Hospice, which opened three weeks before she died.

My mother spent her last few days there, unable at first to believe that this was not some lavish private facility for which I was surreptitiously paying hundreds of pounds. To all the staff who relieved her distress and helped her to achieve a peaceful end – many still working at the hospice – my gratitude is greater than I shall ever be able to express.

After that, it seemed small return to be on call for the hospice one night per week, and indeed the workload over ten years proved negligible. Such was the foresight and expertise shown by the hospice staff that over that period I only needed to visit the ward on a handful of occasions. The rest consisted of infrequent telephone calls to authorise medication or (even rarer) to give advice. The ward nursing staff were painstaking in their anticipation of any distress and difficulty, and more often it was I who learnt from them.

Over recent years I have been able to bring to fruition some of my attempts to promote palliative care for advanced heart failure, including the first book on the topic (currently in press) which I have put together with Miriam Johnson, a palliative care consultant from Scarborough. I have also run national conferences and promoted this aspect of palliative care on a committee of the National Council for Palliative Care. This activity has brought me into contact with many of the leading figures in palliative care from the UK and elsewhere. It has also confirmed my opinion that the residents of North Oxfordshire are truly fortunate to have Katharine House Hospice, which provides care which is the equal of any in the country, or indeed, so far as I know about it, the world.

A volunteer (in many ways!) – Dina Bentley

I had no idea that in 2006 I would still be connected with Katharine House Hospice after my first contact about eighteen years ago. Let me start at the beginning – I was working as Personnel Services Manager at Crest Hotels and was approached to see whether Crest Hotels would be willing to provide office space for the people who were endeavouring to get a hospice built in the Banbury area. I agreed to ask my Director, although I was not over optimistic as, although we were a very large company, most of our Directors did not live locally and were not involved in local projects. However, my Director spoke to our Managing Director who, to my amazement and delight, was more than happy, not only to allocate free office space for the hospice pioneers, but also offered free telephone and fax access, photocopying and other office facilities plus free car parking. Free car parking in the centre of Banbury was a real bonus. It is an amazing co-incidence that these offices were situated right next door to where the Katharine House Hospice shop is now – the rooms were above the archway in the black and white timbered building. During the time the hospice offices were at Crest Hotels I met many of the people involved in the development and planning of the hospice, some still involved, others who have moved on. It was certainly a 'vision' that these pioneers had when starting this project.

In 1990, Crest Hotels was sold to Trust House Forte (THF) and the Head Office in Banbury was closed. I decided that my future was not with THF but lay in another direction and in 1991, the year when Princess Diana opened Katharine House Hospice, I became Practice Manager at Deddington Health Centre and once again renewed my contact with Katharine House but in a different way. No longer was it involvement in the paperwork and development of the hospice but in the nursing care provided by the hospice. Over the years I was at the Health Centre, many of our patients benefited from the day and in-patient care at the hospice and ultimately we had a specialist nurse from the hospice attached to the Health Centre. This was of enormous help both to the patients and the doctors. Most weeks our specialist nurse would visit the Health Centre and have a meeting with the doctors to discuss patient care and during the week she was available to advise and visit patients. This ensured that, in addition to their doctors, patients who were experiencing a very difficult time, had someone to help and support them.

At the time I joined Deddington Health Centre, I decided I would like to help the hospice and became a voluntary evening receptionist. Since retiring in 2003, I have been lucky to be able to increase my voluntary commitment and now help on reception during the day, transport patients to and from the hospice, and also assist with fundraising. I am always made to feel very welcome however little or much I do. I only wish there were more hours in the day for me to offer more help as the hospice provides the most incredible support for both patients, families and friends when life can be very difficult. I have experienced that support when my very close friend was cared for and died in the hospice in 2004. As a patient told me when I was driving him to the hospice for his day care – "Katharine House Hospice is not a 5* hotel, it's even better than a 6* hotel".

I am always pleased when I look back to feel that in a very small way I was able to help in the early stages of planning Katharine House by arranging office accommodation at Crest Hotels and to be able to continue that help now by doing voluntary work at the hospice.

A Consultant Physician, Horton Hospital – Dr. Rolf Smith

It could be said that I am in quite a good position to make some observations about the impact of Katharine House Hospice on the management of patients with terminal disease, partly because I started working at the Horton Hospital some years before the Hospice opened and so can compare the 'then' with the 'now', and partly because my speciality of chest medicine means I treat many people with lung cancer. Most lung cancer patients cannot be cured and I know that for several years they were the largest group treated at the Hospice, although now that many non-malignant conditions are also cared for this may no longer be the case.

Before the Hospice opened, we did our best to give terminally ill patients a peaceful and dignified death. This was largely with drug treatment. In contrast, the services of the Hospice not only draw on the expertise of staff to optimise these drugs in the management of distressing symptoms but also provide a broad range of other facilities and supports which are so important in giving someone a 'good death', both physically and psychologically not only for the benefit of the patients but also their relatives. Linked with this is the fact that whereas in hospital we tend to treat each individual symptom, in the hospice setting, the patient is regarded in a truly 'holistic' way which involves a whole team of carers, each providing their specialist input with attention to detail which can never be provided on an acute medical ward. There is no doubt that terminally ill people, and also those treated as day cases for symptom control, are made to feel that they are very special and that they matter a great deal to the Hospice team.

As you can see from these brief comments, I believe that Katharine House has transformed the quality of care these very deserving patients receive and all the staff at the Horton hold it in very high regard.

An ex-Trustee – Dr. Martin Harris

I first became involved with the move to establish a hospice in the Banbury area when I was asked by Heather Stewart, a good friend in Sibford, to form a pilot group with Neil Gadsby. The only hospice provision in Oxfordshire was Sobell House, run by the doyen of terminal care, Robert Twycross. There was another group thinking about hospice care in Banbury which included George Mason and Richard Adam, Consultant Chest Physician at the Horton Hospital. I remember visiting Neil at his home – I think he wanted to check me out – and was very impressed both by his impartiality at a very difficult time for him, his professionalism and his ethos of personal care which he wanted to engender in the hospice.

The original trustees were a disparate group, Heather and David Stewart, Lynne Simms, Kath and Alan Overton, Jeff Chard, Andrew Edwards, myself and of course Neil. We needed to raise two million pounds somehow. I can remember a moment (after a pig roast with the loan of the Sibford scouts marquee which made £2,000 profit bringing the total raised by then to £10,000) wondering however it could be done. I also remember being worried by doubting Thomas' who thought it was 'pie-in-the-sky'. This was soon after the collapse of the Jimmy Black theatre venture in Banbury. Neil, of course, was always dogged, totally committed and unfazed. We took advice from professional fundraisers. A local committee, chaired by John Bridgeman, and a national committee, chaired by Peter Ward, were set up and money started to trickle in.

Meanwhile we were investigating the setting up of a Bereavement Counselling service. Neil, Richard and I travelled to Leicester where they had a Day Hospice and excellent Bereavement Counselling service. We trained and set up our counselling service with a number of excellent counsellors who were all voluntary. John Simms was appointed Architect and I managed to persuade Richard Adam, recently retired from the NHS, to join the Trustees – a great relief to me to have another doctor's advice. His wisdom and medical expertise were essential in the early days when he became the first Medical Director. John, Richard, Neil and I travelled to many hospices such as Milton Keynes, Myton, Leicester, Sheffield and one or two others, picking the brains of the managers, medical directors and nurses. The result is the beautifully laid-out building you see today on land kindly donated by the Quakers at East House.

The Trustees met fortnightly. We had a common ethos to provide holistic comfort and symptom relief to those with terminal cancer. In particular, we wanted all who worked in the hospice to have this same feeling. This was serious business, but we had lots of laughs and became a very close-knit group. The next step was to persuade the Macmillan charity to fund two Macmillan nurses for three years (after which time the Hospice would pay for them) to start work in the community. Anne Martin, Di Lynch and later Bernadette Ross were wonderful highly trained nurses who became the fronting face of the Hospice. Building started in 1989. We next appointed the first Matron, Elizabeth Phillips-Smith who did a wonderful job in selecting and training the first nurses. The Hospice team at that time was Elizabeth (Matron), Richard Adam (Medical Director – unpaid) and Neil (Administrator – also unpaid). I recruited three other GPs (Richard Lehman, Brendan O'Farrell and George Mason) to run an 'on-call' rota for nights to relieve Richard Adam.

From little pebbles do small mountains grow. What you see today is a highly professional organisation, managed by an executive team offering clinical probity and excellence. This is all the work of a committed bunch of ordinary people in the Banbury area. Alas, I am no longer a Trustee, but I look back in amazement at what we have achieved, and I am quite happy that the hospice is in safe hands.

A Voluntary Driver – Brian Pyart

I was born in Swansea and lived in a small Welsh village where I appeared to be continually running errands for the community without any thought of gain apart from the satisfaction I got from helping others. This trait has remained with me throughout my life, firstly as a bus driver and, for the last 28 years of my working life, as a police officer where I much preferred helping people rather than prosecuting them. No doubt some may disagree with this last sentiment.

I retired in 1989 and after a short spell driving for Age Concern in Newbury, we moved back to Banbury to be closer to our daughters. On a visit to Bodicote post office, I saw a notice asking for volunteer drivers for the Katharine House Hospice, which at that time was only a Day Unit. I had a negative view about illness, especially cancer, but the Matron at that time assured me that if I did take the job and it did affect me in any way, I would always be able to talk to someone. Well, that was 15 years ago, and after more than 100,000 miles, I still love the job and hope I am able to drive for the Katharine House for many years to come.

My work involves collecting patients from their homes in the morning, taking them to the Day Unit and returning them home in the afternoon. Sometimes, this can include the patients' relatives if they have no means of transport. We cover a large area of North Oxfordshire and parts of Northampton and Gloucestershire. Sometimes we transport patients to appointments at the JR2 and Churchill hospitals in Oxford.

Some patients remain fairly quiet during the journey, but the majority are quite chatty. I have a keen sense of humour and at times we have quite a laugh and I seem to build a close relationship with them. I have met some wonderful people during the last 15 years and remember virtually all of them by name.

I recall an incident some years ago when I was asked to take an item to a patient's home. This gentleman was uncertain about coming to the Day Unit. It was around the time that the M40 motorway had just opened and after a short discussion, I offered to take him for a ride on the motorway as he had not seen it. On the way back, I needed to drop in at the Hospice for a minute. He was reluctant to come in with me, but after a short while he agreed. As soon as we entered the sitting room, he recognised an old friend of his, also a patient, and in no time they were chatting quite happily. After informing his wife where he was, I left him and returned in the afternoon to take him home. I enquired if he'd had a good day and he was full of praise for the Hospice telling me what a lovely dinner he'd had. When a nurse asked him if he would like a drink, he thought to himself, I'll be a bit clever here, "I'll have a double brandy please", which a few moments later was duly handed to him by the nurse. From that day on he would worry that if the weather was bad, I would not be able to collect him and take him to the Day Unit.

I love doing the job and always look forward to getting up in the morning. I feel privileged and proud to be a small part of a dedicated team at the Hospice. I have had several offers of well-paid part-time work since retiring, but have declined them because I am happy doing what I do. The job satisfaction far outweighs the monetary gain.

A Trustee (and first Chaplain) – Reverend Jeff Chard

The warmest memories I have of the Hospice, perhaps inevitably, go back to the beginnings. The Trustees met every fortnight on a Wednesday, and I remember those meetings with such affection, not so much for what we achieved, for often, for months on end, there would be very little progress beyond the constant supply of small amounts of money that came in from all sorts of people and organisations across Banburyshire. Compared to the two and a half million pounds we needed, the sums collected seemed so small - £10, £20 or perhaps £150. But it was, I think, these small sums that reminded us how quickly the people of Banbury were taking the Hospice to its heart, and drove us on to seek the larger amounts that would help to complete the buildings. And so what I remember most of the meetings is the warmth and expectation of a small group of ordinary people who shared an extraordinary vision and who were taking and giving more from their togetherness than they ever could from their individuality.

Serious though the venture was, and so sad was the death that was driving it on, yet we had so much fun in those earliest days. Each of us, though I a lot less than some others, took turns at going around the community to receive donations collected in community groups – pubs, village halls, community centres and even private houses. This often gave us the opportunity to talk about Katharine House, and to share our vision, and in turn to be encouraged by the affection, warmth and commitment so many in the community were giving us.

As Chaplain in those first days of the Hospice, so many of my memories are there. Before the building finished – while plasterers and painters were still working, before the heating was installed or carpets laid – Christmas came and we decided to hold a Carol Service in the Chapel. Seventy or so people turned up. We borrowed some portable heaters, and each person brought with them a garden chair. The Chapel could not hold us all and we spread out into the corridor, which was very cold indeed! One of our Trustees, David Stewart, brought and played a keyboard. What an evening! It was the first time the Hospice had been used and for me it celebrated the optimism of the Trustees and volunteers of the Hospice and of my Christian faith. By the time the next Christmas came the Hospice was up and running and the Carol Service was held for the 'day-patients', on the morning of their Christmas lunch. Neil Gadsby dressed up (as he still does) as Father Christmas to deliver presents to everyone before he carved the turkey!

The first year that the Hospice opened fully, now with a full complement of nurses, we decided to hold our Carol Service at Banbury's Parish Church. This building holds two thousand people, and I was surprised (but I should not have been) at the five hundred or more people that came. The nurses provided a choir and walked in procession, carrying candles. One of the nurses had been a professional singer, and many of them had lovely voices, and I will remember to this day trying to cope with Darke's version of 'In the bleak midwinter' with its top note at the end. Those Carol Services with the nurses' choir and various members of the Hospice community, including of course the patients, reading the lessons, were a precious time for me and provide now many precious memories. Latterly they have been replaced by the Lights of Love service, when after lighting up the Christmas tree in Horsefair, we all move across the street to St. Mary's Church for what is often a very moving service – but without the nurses' choir.

The Chapel has seen many events. A baptism and marriage have taken place there; every Christmas the Bishop of Dorchester comes to lead our Christmas morning service; and the furniture, the altar and Paschal candle in particular, have been made with such tender care – the altar by a local craftsman, and the Pascal candle by an eighteen year old schoolboy from Bloxham. Every year the chapel hosts a multitude of small concerts, countless meetings, and is always transformed for the Christmas pantomime or show when nurses and doctors dress up and make a fool of themselves to the great amusement of the patients.

Looking back over the twenty-one years since we first signed the Trust Deed there are so many occasions and funny incidents to remember. But my chief memories inevitably are about people. About the small group of Trustees who kept the idea of the Hospice alive when the millions of pounds needed seemed so far away. Of Neil Gadsby, Katharine's father and our Chairman, whose humour and humanity alongside his dedication did more than anything to ensure that the idea came to life. Of all those volunteers and Hospice staff who make Katharine House what it is. Dearest of all, I hold tight to those memories of the Hospice patients I have known over fifteen years. When I haven't known what to say to them, which is quite often, they speak to me. When I want to cry with them, they make me laugh. Their sheer zest for life and their bravery and integrity make me better than I could ever be without them. I think those who do not know the place can have little idea of the fun and vitality, the sheer life that exists in the Hospice. And it touches all of us who are there (supposedly) to help, but who receive so much more in return.

A General Practitioner – Dr Sue Ruddock

Katharine House and its staff and volunteers provide a valuable resource to patients, relatives and carers at any stage of the patient's illness from diagnosis through potentially curative treatments, to palliative care during the terminal phase of their illness to death. Help is then continued afterwards with bereavement support to relatives, friends and carers. It includes support for the patient's children, again through all stages of the illness and after death. Much of this support is provided through the specialist nurses, one of whom is attached to each general practice in the area. There is also access to medical palliative care advice, particularly if control of a patient's symptoms is proving difficult, from the team of palliative care physicians who work at Katharine House.

Katharine House itself provides an excellent patient-centred range of services. Situated in a pleasant setting with a well maintained garden where patients feel at ease, aided by excellent home cooking, tropical fish, a bar, pet dog and piano recital sessions, its flexibility caters for patients experiencing cancer and other terminal illnesses including heart failure and motor neurone disease. It offers practical help either as an inpatient or day care for an enormous range of needs from bathing through complementary therapies including aromatherapy, reflexology and massage, to the lymphoedema clinics which help many patients with swollen limbs from a variety of causes. Patients may also be admitted for procedures including blood transfusions and drainage of fluid from chest and abdominal cavities. Spiritual support of any kind is available, as is advice regarding benefits and charitable monies which may be available to patients, legal advice for wills and ultimately help with funeral arrangements.

For in-patients, freedom of visiting is much appreciated for both family and pets, with flexibility of hours, but staff will bar visitors when appropriate as requested by the patient or family.

Katharine House, largely through the hard work, dedication and expertise of the nurses, makes a hugely positive impact on patient care throughout all stages of their illness and is much appreciated by patients, relatives, friends and carers, and health care professionals.

A General Practitioner – Dr. Brendan O'Farrell

When I arrived in Banbury in 1976, there were no specialists in care of the terminally ill around and there was a general state of ignorance about what could be done. The idea, that strong painkillers only came by injection, pervaded amongst some doctors. Many doctors found it hard to talk about dying. Many patients were ignorant of their diagnosis.

I had been influenced, by some information leaflets emanating from St. Christopher's Hospice and also by an extremely good presentation by a palliative care doctor, on my day-release course when I was a registrar. With a very caring team of district nurses, we managed many of our patients at home to the very end although the conditions at home were not always satisfactory. Care of these patients in an ordinary hospital ward left a lot more to be desired. Michael Sobell House opened and some of our patients were able to go there for their terminal care.

I was involved in starting the Banbury branch of CRUSE although our original set-up was not satisfactory and the branch closed down. It has since been reborn and has thrived. When the original steering committee became the management committee, somebody suggested that we should think about promoting day-care for people with terminal illnesses. Someone then heard a rumour that a group had been formed in the area to promote the development of our own hospice. Two members of the group, Jeff Chard and George Mason, were deputed to make contact with this group so that efforts could be combined. That was the last we saw of Jeff.

The first landmark in improved palliative care was the appointment of Macmillan nurses, now managed by Katharine House, who would be able to talk with patients and advise the nurses and doctors about management. At this time, many general practitioners did not take kindly to being advised by nurses, so in many areas this new breed of specialist nurse had difficulties being accepted. The transition in Banbury went better than expected.

When I walk into Katharine House I now wonder how we managed in the past. We have a centre of excellence where staff are fully up-to-date with the physical and psychological care of our patients. The specialist nurses can bring this expertise straight to our patients who may benefit from the day hospice or in-patient facilities but may stay at home until the end and there is a team of visitors who are available to support the bereaved.

The Building - note from the Architect (following an article published by the RIBA)

The architects, Hallet Design, were included in 1985 in very early discussions of the Trustees regarding the creation of this new hospice, and accompanied the Trustees on many visits to other hospices as the ethos and spatial requirements of Katharine House were decided upon.

The building was to provide 12 beds for in-patient care and also the needs of 10-12 day patients, plus all necessary specialist ancillary accommodation and administration areas. The building also had to be friendly internally and externally, warm and welcoming, to be light and provide patients with a feeling of care, but not to look at all 'medical', and be interlinked with the gardens to help patients to look outward, both physically and spiritually.

No monies were available from Health Authority sources, so all funds had to be raised by the Trustees, who were given two moments of encouragement early on in their fund raising with the offer of a site near Banbury, and the offer from another local Memorial Trust to provide and maintain the formal gardens.

The site was ideal – sloping down from south to north, in three acres of pasture with mature trees on and around it. The architects opted for a linear plan, rather than the courtyard plan that was prevalent at the time but, by turning the plan through angles, were able to create corridors internally that were visually short, and externally to give an 'embracing' feel to the main garden area. With the cruciform plan at the bedroom end, which gives the nursing staff easy control of the area but also allows each bedroom wing its own aspect of the gardens, the plan fulfilled another important feature – from no external point could all the elements be seen, the building therefore looks far smaller than it is, thus its visual 'size' is more friendly to the visitor.

As the site is at the edge of the village of Adderbury, and is seen over open fields, it was decided that the proportions of the building should be agricultural, and this led to the use of low eaves and first floor accommodation with the roof area, and also of two and single-storey elements to help let the building 'grow' out of the site. The external materials of Baggeridge Clent Russet bricks and Rosemary mixed brindle clay tiles were chosen for their warmth of colour and ability to form interesting details, as the inclusion of details adds to the 'friendliness' of the building. But the details all have a purpose – such as the angled bricks at the door and window openings which are to remove the sharp square brick edge should anyone fall against them, or the brick paving pattern under the covered walkway which has patterns outside each door intended to draw the eye and the person to the garden.

To link the building with the garden, all major rooms, including all bedrooms, have doors opening directly onto a covered walkway, onto which chairs or beds can be taken. This provides a covered external route from the bedrooms to the sitting rooms as an alternative to the internal corridor. The walkway is constructed of timber as a natural material, and with the retaining wall creates a cloistered feel between building and garden. The importance of the south-north slope of the site is now apparent as the retaining wall is at a height to allow wheelchair patients to smell or pick flowers, but the full beauty of the garden can still be seen from all patient sitting rooms and bedrooms as the garden slopes down to them.

Internally, the south side of the building is given mainly to patients' sitting areas and bedrooms, with full access to the gardens. Various sitting areas have been included throughout the building, each with a different feel and décor to give patients choice, and windows are low-cilled to give maximum vision when seated. The main sitting room has a full height antique pine fire surround and a fireplace to create a homely atmosphere, and opens out into a heated conservatory and then to the garden. The north side contains the specialist bathrooms, treatment rooms and toilets, and also a reception room and chapel with vestry, but these areas have also been given thought with such details as the use of slightly bronzed mirrors to the bath and treatment rooms to make the patients look more healthy and therefore maybe feel happier in themselves. The reception room is to allow new patients time to spend with their families and meet the nursing staff before being taken to the bedrooms. It will also be used as a 'snooze' room where day patients may rest or sleep in a bed or easy chairs if they get tired during their stay, hence being on the north side away from the sunshine. The chapel, vestry and quiet room are situated between day-care and bedroom areas. The quiet room is where bereaved relatives may say their goodbyes to the deceased, and adjacent is the vestry where they may talk with staff or counsellors or be alone. They may also use the small private walled garden which can only be entered through the vestry. The chapel can be used in its hexagonal shape for small services or discussions, or opened up to include the foyer for other events.

One feature of the layout is that beds may be taken into any of the sitting areas and the chapel and even the hairdressing room, so that patients confined to bed may also have their hair done if desired. The bedrooms include two four-bedded rooms, two single-rooms and two family-rooms, which are furnished with double or single beds and bed settees as required for individual families to stay together as long as possible. Again all bedroom windows are low-cilled so that there is a view of the garden from all beds, even when lying down.

The first floor is over the day-care part of the building, not over the bedrooms, and includes office accommodation, staff changing rooms and toilets, a library/study room, and a teaching/dining room which will be used for ongoing training for all staff and outside volunteers. It will also be used as the alternative dining room, away from the patient dining room, that is required for registration as a Nursing Home. These staff areas are also intended to give the staff the feeling of being cared for in the same way as they care for the patients, with the rooms being of interesting shapes and the use of colourful wall tiling in the changing rooms and toilets. Also at first floor is the gas-fired boiler room (to save valuable ground floor patient space), extension space for future offices or other use, and a small overnight-stay room comprising kitchen/diner and bed/sitting room where any relatives may stay to be close to the patient. The adjacent staircase is therefore fitted with a Gimson Spiralift to cater for any disabled relative, and this also allows any wheelchair-bound staff to work in all areas of the hospice.

Floors throughout are covered with Steeles Carpets' Datum Twist carpet, except wet areas which are Altro safety floor. The colour scheme is of gentle, warm colours to the ground floor, with brighter colours to the first floor staff areas, and decorative lighting to all public/patient areas has been supplied by two local manufacturers – David Hunt and DAR.

The external areas outside the formal garden are to be planted as a wild flower meadow with earth banking and several copses of trees to provide sheltered sitting areas, and a duck pond is included for extra interest, as is a dovecote in the boiler room half-gable. The service entrance is hidden from the main entrance and chapel garden by a natural stone wall which slopes down to meet a small entrance gate, thus providing the necessary screening but not restricting the view of the pedestrian entrance and access drive, which may have given visitors a feeling of being 'cut off' from the world.

The Simon Weatherby Garden - Caroline Weatherby

"I thought of all the joys which the sense of sight brings me, the enjoyment of my garden particularly. The pleasure I get from just sitting there in a brown study, enjoying the colours, the contrasts of texture, the harmony, and the thoughts of all the things I want to do to improve what I see."
Excerpt from Simon Weatherby's journal January 26th 1977

The story behind the beautiful garden at Katharine House Hospice began in 1985. For two years, since my husband Simon's death, I had been trying to find the right vehicle for a memorial to him. My first idea, which was to do something bringing complementary and allopathic medicine together (sparked by the fact that Simon had so much help using both), had failed. I was therefore feeling a bit despondent, when a friend suddenly said, with a flash of inspiration, "Simon loved gardening, why don't you create a garden in his memory?" Instantly I knew that was it. "You're a genius!", I told him. "And furthermore I know just where it should be".

Earlier that day I had been much struck by a brochure I had received about a hospice to be built in Adderbury near Banbury. I went straight to my desk to get it and dialled the number on the bottom of the page. Heather Gadsby answered the telephone. I told her I had received the brochure for Katharine House and asked if they were going to have a garden there. Yes, definitely, came the response. As I told her about Simon and my idea of a garden in his memory at the hospice I immediately felt her warmth and enthusiasm. She and Neil ended up coming to lunch on Sunday and we spent the whole afternoon discussing the hospice and the garden.

I learnt that Katharine and Simon had both shared a love of music and poetry, a terrific sense of humour, and a strong faith and belief in a bigger purpose behind what was happening to them and their illness. I had such respect for Heather and Neil, who had suffered the unbelievable grief of losing an only child and were now putting all their energy into this hugely ambitious project to make things better for others in their position. My idea seemed puny by comparison, but they were so thrilled and so grateful and we parted the best of friends.

Neil and Heather went to put the idea of the Simon Weatherby Garden to their Trustees, and I went in search of a committee to help fundraise and plan the garden. My enthusiasm was slightly blunted as friends and family members said they would support it but couldn't help on the ground. However, I did find three kind friends who agreed to a meeting, at the end of which we had a secretary, a treasurer and a chairman, so that was a beginning. These friends, as one so often finds, were all busy people and I am eternally grateful to them. They were Ann Harper, Claire Menzies Kitchin and the one person who made the whole thing possible really, Patrick (Pat) Braddell.

I should at this point say that Simon didn't just love gardening, it was his passion and he spent every possible waking moment doing it. If he was lost in thought and I was to say "What are you thinking?", nine times out of ten it would be about some aspect of the garden. I can safely say the garden was the "other woman" in our relationship, and here I was trying to create another one for him! Pat, like Simon, was a keen and talented amateur gardener and their ideas were along similar lines, I knew if I could get Pat on board we'd be alright. I often wonder what he thought in those early days of planning; unfortunately it is too late to ask him as he sadly died in June this year, but I suspect he thought it was a pie-in-the-sky idea and would just fade away.

At the first few meetings the "you" and "your" word was always used - "What are you going to do about such and such?", "You're going to have to raise the money first", etc. I longed for the "we" word. I told them I planned to send out a letter to family, friends, and Simon's colleagues in the horseracing world. Simon worked in the family firm of Weatherby and Sons and was secretary to the Jockey Club, a post that had been held by a Mr Weatherby since the eighteenth century. The youngest man ever to hold this position, he was immensely popular and contributed much to the sport, so I knew they would be supportive.

It always amused me that like their horses, the industry also bred its racing officials, at least in this instance. Simon told me that way back when the Duke of Queensberry had raced his thoroughbred against the Earl of Derby, a Mr Weatherby held the stake, and one or other of them has been doing so ever since. In the eighteenth century, one of his successors also started the famous Weatherby's Stud Book, to which every thoroughbred horse must be able to trace its lineage even to this day. But I digress.

My son Max, then 19, had helped me buy a computer. He taught me how to do Mail Merge and we sent out hundreds of letters to everyone we knew, including every racing colleague of Simon's. The response was more than we could have imagined and the letters and cheques started pouring in. I was very excited. It was when I told Pat we had received £5,000 in donations that he said "Now we can start looking for a garden designer" and my heart lifted at the use of the "we" word. "*We* need to open a bank account first", I said. "I'll jump to it!" he replied, grinning.

The next step was to find a designer for the garden, for how could we not match this beautiful building with anything other than a top notch garden? Pat and I went and looked at several hospice gardens, including Trinity House in London and the Sue Rider Hospice in Cheltenham, to get ideas. These two in particular were lovely and beautifully cared for by dedicated teams of gardeners, but none had the advantage we had with John Sims' building design, which had the building curving around the garden so it could be looked out on from every room, with a veranda onto which patients beds could be wheeled on warm sunny days.

We decided to ask three people to offer a garden design, and we would choose the one we liked best. Chelsea gold medallist Jane Fearnley Whittingstall's was the one we chose. We showed it to Neil, Heather and the Trustees for the hospice, and they all liked it. Not only was it a beautiful design, but Jane is a real plantswoman as well and had included a lot of Simon's favourite plants, with softer colours near the bedrooms and brighter ones further away. I really wanted water and she had put a stream running through the garden into a pond, with the sound of gently falling water, which is so healing.

I remember her coming to what was then a building site, in the middle of a field, and we crouched down among the rubble with her designs spread out before us. It was hard to imagine it would ever be a garden! We took a picture for posterity.

We still had some time to wait while the hospice was being built before we could start on the garden, during which time the fundraising continued. Friends joined in; in particular the artist Hugh Dunford Wood did a lovely logo for us, my neighbour Judy Young had some Simon Weatherby Garden T shirts made to sell, and her husband Kenny, who is a song writer and recording engineer, recorded me singing songs with guitar for a cassette which we called 'Songs for Simon's Garden'. I did this with the help of cellist Emily Burrage and Brian Gulland on the keyboard. We had a lot of fun making it and have all remained friends since.

It's wonderful how projects like this bring people together and the offshoots that come as a result of shared giving. Another such came through the publishing of Simon's Commonplace Book, in which he had jotted down readings and passages from books which struck him or moved him in some way. I have had many letters and donations from total strangers who have come across that little book. One person found it by his bed in a B&B, another in a friend's loo!

My friend, the newsreader Richard Baker, and I did several concerts to raise funds; we had performed together in programmes of words and music, one of which had been devised for us by Simon, for many years. One of these concerts, I remember, was at Batsford House near Moreton–in–Marsh, kindly lent to us by Lord and Lady Dulverton. The concert was well under way and Richard was reading, when Lord Dulverton, who was fairly old and probably rather deaf, said in ringing tones, "Is that man Baker still going on?" Richard, quite undaunted, said "Well, I've got one more page but I'll try and hurry it up!" which brought the house down. Somebody once said that if a leg fell off the piano Richard would carry it off.

At last, with £33,000 now in our coffers, the time came when we could start the garden. Jane Fearnley Whittingstall suggested Andrew Neville from Cheltenham to carry out the work, which was an excellent choice. He and his team were professional and efficient as well as extremely nice. The intricate network of paths, which had to be wide enough for wheel chairs, was to be done by a local contractor. Possibly this was a mistake, as the paths were the only thing that went wrong and had to be redone, causing a bit of a rumpus and more expense.

But we couldn't complain; the rubble and mess disappeared and the garden unfolded before our eyes. Pond and stream, paths, borders, shrubs and trees all appeared as if by magic. There were trellises with roses growing up the posts of the veranda, overlooking a mosaic of tiny plants in a sea of rich brown earth. Then the lawns were laid and suddenly it was a garden. Because global warming even then was looming, we put in an irrigation system so beds could be watered by turning on a switch.

One of the great successes of the garden is the pond, mainly due to Pat's discovery of Bill Heritage. Bill, an acknowledged expert on creating ponds, has written two books on the subject which Pat had read. Pat contacted him through the publisher and another friend was made. He not only advised us but came out to the hospice himself to oversee the work, for which we are eternally grateful. He explained how important it is to get the right ratio of surface water to depth of the pond, to ensure the right balance - then it can maintain itself and the water remains clear. So many ponds start off looking lovely and then cloud over becoming unsightly and sickly looking. Thanks to Bill ours never has and is full of large healthy looking goldfish! I gather Bill's book is still available if anyone is needing advice about putting in a pond.

As the process was drawing to a close, a sudden thought struck me, who was going to look after the garden? I rang Pat. "We need gardeners" I said. "How are we going to find people to help look after it?" "Oh I've thought of that", he said in his slow drawl. "I've put an ad in the Banbury Guardian." Eight people answered the advertisement, most of whom are still coming every Thursday to care for the garden. All are volunteers, who do it for love. They are definitely the unsung heroes and heroines of the story, for without them there would be no garden today.

Our story is now nearly at an end. The garden was completed in 1991 but was officially opened by Richard Baker in July 1992. We decided to wait a year to give the plants a chance to get going. Everyone who saw it was astonished at the speed with which everything had grown in that time.

It has developed and blossomed over the years, thanks to the devotion and hard work of Pat and his team. It is also a testament to Jane Fearnley Whittingstall's design that there have been very few changes needed along the way. A lovely octagonal garden was added at the top end, designed by Pat. It is surrounded by a hedge with a fountain in the middle, which gives privacy for anyone wanting to be alone and not overlooked. Another addition is two sculptures by local sculptress Sophie Thompson, of a sheep and a goat, which look enchanting grazing nonchalantly by the pond!

The management of the garden, always handled with the lightest touch by Pat Braddell (I asked him once if the gardeners were given specific tasks to do each Thursday and he said no, everyone just does what they feel like!) has passed into the capable hands of Helen Lamb. Helen, a true gardener in every sense, was professionally trained at Wisley, and we are terribly lucky to have her. We are also lucky to have Helen's father, Trevor Sprittlehouse, who also works in the garden and has taken over Pat's other job of Treasurer.

We have an open day every June, which has become a popular event at the hospice. This keeps our coffers topped up and allows us to share the Simon Weatherby Garden with a larger public. But apart from that one day, the garden is for the enjoyment of patients and their families and the staff of Katharine House, a gift of beauty and love.

Memories of compiling 'Superhints' books for the Katharine House Hospice – Audrey, The Lady Wardington

My great friend and secretary, Marion Shaw, died quite quickly of cancer in 1989. I was deeply saddened by her death but it had a lasting effect on my life in two ways. I learnt about the Hospice movement from seeing how wonderfully she was tended until her death and I fell deeply in love with my Amstrad word-processor which I bought in a fruitless effort to replace her. I read in the local paper about plans for a Hospice in Banbury and wished I could think of a way of helping to raise money for it; I longed to make proper use of my Amstrad – perhaps write a book!

To cut a long story short, I came up with something which encompassed both my interests. A book of hints for every kind of eventuality, collected from famous, titled or interesting people. I was thrilled with the idea and managed to interest my great friend, Laurie Purden, who had just retired from editing 'Woman's Journal' and was prepared to help me with her journalistic expertise. We had thought that perhaps we should try to interest a literary agent but when

I mentioned the idea to my sister-in-law, who was a literary agent, she drowned us with cold water and suggested a collection of letters of condolence might be better! We ignored her advice and put together a nice selection of hints – one I remember, was to plant daffodil bulbs in mashed beetroot; result, pink daffodils! – and tacked very 'good names' to them. We typed it all out to look professional and sent it to six publishers with a covering letter explaining that we wanted the book published to raise money for our local hospice. Five bundles flopped back through the letter box, but wonder of wonders, instead of the sixth, was a letter from Michael Joseph, part of the Penguin group, suggesting I call and see them.

Dizzy with excitement, I arranged terms, royalties, etc. (luckily I knew that I must make every penny over to the Hospice before I started as, if I received any of the proceeds, I would have to pay tax on it before the Hospice got a penny) and it was only at this stage that I went to see Neil Gadsby to tell him of my plan. I think he was a bit bewildered. He was very busy getting the Hospice started, a daunting task and a labour of love. I explained that I would not expect or want any help from his team and since he could see no harm in it, he made enthusiastic noises and away we went.

We spent the next six months collecting hints, I wrote to everyone I knew and friends gave me names and addresses of all their celebrity friends and acquaintances. I wrote hundreds of letters explaining my project and enclosing a nice list of hints I had already received from famous people as a guide – these were *bona fide*. People were wonderful. Princess Margaret suggested that the best way to get rid of a red wine stain was by pouring white wine on it. Paul Eddington cleaned his brass door knob with Worcestershire Sauce and Mrs Thatcher (as she was then) recommended her way of beating jet lag. I became obsessed with hints, collecting them from everyone I spoke to, including the window cleaner, plumber and postman! All this time, I heard nothing from Michael Joseph. I rang nervously, asking if they really wanted the book. They assured me they did, in fact it already had a British Library number and they expected the finished work in March for publication in November. We finished it in time, Laurie correcting my whimsical spelling and weird punctuation. My Amstrad fulfilled its expectations, giving me the ability to whisk hints back and forth, which I so enjoyed doing – though I have to admit occasionally one got lost in transit. I'm ashamed to say that I never tested any of the hints but there was a ferocious disclaimer in the front of the book. The publishers gave it the final OK, illustrations were chosen and the dust jacket was designed. The wording on the cover took almost as much effort as writing the whole book.

'Superhints' was published in November 1992, the same year that the Hospice was officially opened by Princess Diana – I had the honour of presenting her with a copy – and such were the reviews and publicity that the first 2,000 copies sold out in a week. We had to wait three weeks for a reprint of 2,000 more and another three weeks for a further reprint. Everyone, apart from Laurie and I, was amazed.

We went from strength to strength. A new early morning television show had started called 'The Big Breakfast'. Contributors to 'Superhints' were invited to appear on the show, demonstrating their hints. Thrilled, I got up at six every morning for a week to watch 'Superhints' being aired, but to my fury, there was no mention of the book or the charity. I remonstrated with the company, to no avail, and finally wrote to Bob Geldof, who was a backer of the show, complaining that all my contributors had given their hints to help the charity and now appearing on television, thinking they were still helping, but since the viewing public were not told where the hints came from, they were being exploited. I got a sweet note back from him, written on a crumpled piece of paper torn out of a notebook, sympathising. Within a week, we had a donation of £5,000 and a mention with every hint. The publisher changed the dust jacket to accommodate a banner 'As seen on television'!

After that, I negotiated a deal whereby the Hospice could buy the books directly from Michael Joseph at the wholesale price, and sell them themselves, thus making £5 on every book sold plus the 7.5% royalty.

In 1993 I compiled 'Superhints for Gardeners' which was really the most successful of the four books and it remained in print for ten years. 'Superhints for Cooks' came out in 1994 and among its contributors were many chefs who are now well known on television but in those days were just working in top restaurants. I wrote to every three, four and five star establishment in my quest for tips on success in the kitchen.

Finally in 1997 I compiled 'Superhints for Life', which I wanted to be more philosophical with hints on love, life and marriage, but the publishers, who had really lost interest at this time, wanted the same old format. It still sold quite well. I'm not sure that anyone ever actually read the books but they were wonderful presents. All in all the books made well over £100,000 for the Hospice and I had thoroughly enjoyed my adventure into the publishing world.

Along the way, I saw the wonderful work the Katharine House Hospice achieved, watching it grow over the years under the dedicated eye of its founder, Neil Gadsby.

Coffee and Chat – Iris Collier

The origins of 'Coffee and Chat' in Adderbury began in 1991, the outcome of a Bible Study Group where ways of getting lonely people, young mothers and village newcomers together socially in Church House had been discussed. Although there was opposition, four determined ladies persevered and 'Coffee and Chat' was born.

The number of visitors rose quite quickly and as they wanted to contribute money, a bowl was put out for donations. It was very exciting, when, as early as May 1992, £500 had accrued and was presented to the Katharine House Hospice. Adderbury's own Village Millennium was in 1995 and Church House gave over £1,000 to the Celebrations Fund, a donation to the Horton's Cancer Research Centre and money for church flowers.

Between 1998/2000, Church House was completely renovated to provide for a library, so 'Coffee and Chat' was moved to the Methodist Schoolroom in Chapel Lane. The room had been newly decorated and we quickly raised £350 to have a hatch built between the kitchen and the schoolroom. There was more space than before and so the number of visitors kept on increasing. When the library was finished, there was not enough room for everybody, so both "Coffee and Chat" venues continued but with finances kept separate and all their donations for the Hospice.

The first day 'on our own' was October 3rd 2000, and the Methodist Schoolroom took a massive £92.50. Throughout the growing season, we have a steady supply of fresh produce and plants, plus jams and chutneys. There is a mass exodus from chairs to the table as these goodies arrive and nothing stays there for long. Two of our younger supporters buy all the tea, coffee and sugar and at least twice a year hold raffles for which they provide all the prizes including fresh flower arrangements appropriate to the season. Another regular visitor bought lovely royal blue cloths for the tables – "so we look more co-ordinated".

The coffee-makers at both 'Coffee and Chat' venues provide milk and biscuits and also flowers for the tables. Each venue has a rota for their own people and at the schoolroom we also have one for the bric-a-brac table. As many ladies (and one gentleman) are on all three lists it can be a nightmare ensuring no-one ends up in three places at once (it did happen!). We are open every Tuesday from 10 am to 12 noon. One day in late November, as we were clearing up, the door opened and about twenty sock-wearing hikers arrived. They had lined up their boots in the lane outside. More milk was hastily bought from the butcher's and their purchases nearly doubled our income that morning. We are now being included in a new 'Adderbury Walks' pamphlet.

Up until 2006, £11,000 has been donated from Church House to the hospice. Between October 2000 and February 2006, the Methodist Schoolroom group has donated £13,000 and it has been a pleasure so to do. The original aims of 1991 have more than been fulfilled with two places for neighbours and friends to meet for a chat.

Cottage Crafts of Tadmarton – Peter and Margaret Whittle

It is easier to explain about Cottage Crafts if we sketch in a little of our background. Through varying circumstances, we had five children under five years which meant we were very busy and very poor, especially as they grew older. This state of affairs encouraged us to make toys and clothes for them; everything was also home-cooked: bread, soup, jam, cakes, sweets for birthdays.......

Years later when we retired, our youngest daughter, Ursula, who was earning a living selling her jewellery at craft fairs, suggested we revived our skills for a good cause. Katharine House, which had just been opened by Princess Diana, seemed the right one. She also recommended that we sell from home as people might come because they were curious to see what our cottage looked like. In 1993, Cottage Crafts was born.

Ursula assured us that she would come with her jewellery so we need not worry about how many things we could make. She also wanted to give us a high percentage of what she took herself. Peter was flummoxed. He had only ever made <u>one</u> of anything. Margaret was worried too. Her patchwork cushions took days to make (they still do) and she was unsure what people would buy of anything else she made, such as placemats, cafetiére cloaks and wheat warmers. A two-day event was planned: a trestle table with the crafts on it was set up in the sitting room, and the furniture moved to the walls. There was no charge to come in and a cup of tea was available to buy in the kitchen. We worried that no one would come. Ursula set up her jewellery and the other three daughters came to help. Apart from four couples who came in, had a look round the cottage and left without buying anything, it was an amazing event : 350 people visited and the Hospice was given £1300 from the weekend. From then on, we charged to come in and the tea was free.

As word got around, the event grew year by year. We experimented with new ideas; Peter made more neo-Victorian toys and each year the magazine, The Woodworker, accepted one of the designs he sent them for publication.

During the thirteen years we held the event at the cottage, it grew beyond recognition. The furniture was moved out of the rooms so that stalls of our crafts could be set up. We used the upstairs landing as a selling area and erected two marquees in the garden as sitting places for drinking tea or having home-made soup. We made it a three-day event hoping to ease the rush, but it meant that just more people came. Then Tadmarton supporters arrived to pack the goods through the months and run the kitchen during the weekend: the 'Helping Hands' were born. The farmer allowed his field to be used for parking, people made biscuits, cakes for the Bring and Buy, a quilt to be raffled. It became a community effort.

We produced an enormous variety of things each year – some sixty lines in all – as well as a thousand jars of jams and chutneys, and five hundred packets of fudge. Finally we realised it was becoming too much and we could no longer manage to use the cottage to host the event, but that was after we had had over nine thousand people coming over the thirteen years and given the Hospice £74,091 during that time. It was wonderful to do it.

Bicester Friends – Georgina Lamb, Honorary Treasurer 1991 to date

In the early eighties a group of friends were having keep-fit classes organised by the late Mrs. Leonie Richards but when the classes were abandoned, Mrs. Jenny Phillips invited the ten class members to lunch. This developed into a regular event every month and continues to this day with all taking it in turns to be the hostess. Sadly now we are only eight.

After a while, we thought it would be nice to make the lunches into a meeting and have a speaker or make a contribution to a charity. We all supported different appeals and organisations so decided to just support one thing and Katharine House Hospice was chosen as it was just in the planning stage and we had heard about it on Radio Oxford that morning. Over the twenty-two years we have had hundreds of lunches, which we all enjoy and look forward to every month, and have been able to make £16,658 for the Hospice. It is a great challenge to find different things to serve but not many times have dishes been duplicated. Twice a year, we invite guests to join us. In June, we meet on Ladies Ascot Day and this is always well supported. One year, several Luncheon Ladies were going to the actual races and so the rest decided to invite a friend and 'pretend' we were also going by dressing up and wearing our wedding hats, etc., and this tradition has continued. At Christmas we have two guests and organise a sumptuous meal with hats and gifts and this also helps to make extra money for the Hospice. There are now three other luncheon groups, and on one occasion we all got together at the Great Barn in Aynho for a joint lunch.

At one of our earlier lunches, Leonie, who was a strong supporter of the Hospice, decided that she would form a committee to raise funds by organising different events. Jenny Phillips, Carolinda Maitland and myself agreed to serve on this committee together with about five others from outside the lunch group. This committee was formed in 1987 and the first event was a musical evening at Bucknell Manor which raised £332. During its nineteen years existence there have been five chairpersons – Leonie Richards, Carolinda Maitland, Jennie Candy, Nella Garton and now Jane Jones – and the group has managed to raise nearly £200,000. There have been many members come and go over the years and this helps to stimulate interest in different areas, age groups and functions.

The two biggest events were a gambling evening and dance at North Aston Hall and a dinner at Farnborough Hall. Our regular events which prove popular are the Reels evening, the Spring Fair, the Clay Pigeon Shoot and Neverkeneza (a young people's dance) but we have also had bridge and whist drives, cycle rides followed by a BBQ, sponsored cricket matches, fashion shows, Christmas musical evenings and children's parties.

ALMOST THE LAST WORD

From Bernadette Ross, Director of Nursing

I have been honoured to see a draft of this memoir prior to publication. For those, such as myself, with poor memories it can waft one back to float through happy and interesting events as well as serve to fill the gaps where detail was hazy or incomplete at the time. As I rest it down though, I am conscious of something much greater than this. I am heartened to have my belief strengthened that out of great tragedy can emerge immense good.

Those of us who are (just!) old enough to remember the days of doctors ward rounds that passed by those with advanced illness, for there was 'nothing more they could do', are deeply grateful to pioneers such as Dame Cicely Saunders and Elizabeth Kubler-Ross for their vision, insight, stamina and determination, driven perhaps by a power beyond their own. Without these people the hospice movement may never have become a reality, and the lives of similar patients and families would remain filled with pain, distress and a lack of fulfilment and hope. There are however countless other unsung names that collectively understood the hospice philosophy, kept the torch burning or pioneered themselves. Neil Gadsby is one of these. His contribution to the hospice movement has been far greater than many would know and of course without him, Heather and their friends, Katharine House would not exist.

I came to this area from a most wonderful, warm oasis of a hospice in the thick of the noise, bustle and sometimes violence of Hackney. My first impressions of Katharine House were of the space, beauty and peace of the setting, and the completed facilities soon took on a similar vein. Was this too beautiful I asked myself. Not at all, environment is important to all of us – we respond to it and we understand the love that imbibes the hospitality that it displays, the walls somehow infectious with it.

I also wondered whether the care would really be as I had experienced in London. However, it was not long before the detail of this hospice philosophy was clearly established, mainly through the clarity of Elizabeth Phillips-Smith and Richard Adam. What has, however, become increasingly clear to me over the years is the remarkable nature of Neil himself, who has devoted himself to this organisation, steered it wisely, maintained an overarching influence on the philosophy from a place of truly knowing what was important and yet has never interfered nor imposed his personal view on anyone else.

It is difficult to imagine how in those early days of opening our time was not fully utilised, particularly when I see how busy everyone is now, but then we have grown from caring for one patient to about two hundred and fifty at any one time. While a core of staff has remained the same over these first fifteen years, others have come and gone. It is nice to think that they, and those we have offered educational opportunities to, have taken a little bit of the hospice philosophy into other areas, thus extending even further the arms of support of Katharine House.

Working in palliative care, where patients and families face the most vulnerable times in their lives, has been an enormous privilege for me. Unfortunately one that is so very difficult to articulate. While one can witness extremes of sadness, my overriding experience is that of humanity in its fullness graced with a beauty, depth and resilience that we so often miss in our everyday lives. It is as though, rather than becoming dim, the light goes on. This is not to romanticise the pain of suffering, but rather to see the value of life, every life, the uniqueness of each, and the sustenance of small gestures when they are made with love.

I know what a difference this care can make. I am torn between a belief in the 'specialist' nature of the work delivered through the development of skills in recognised practitioners, with a belief that walking alongside, truly being present through the good and the bad, is what matters most and is not much to ask of us as fellow humans. I suspect the best care lies when the two come together, but I hope we never lose the latter to the former. Katharine House somehow seems to capture the importance of both in its gentle cocoon and its wide range of participants who all bring their own gifts.

When we have come thus far, where next I ask? It does seem to me however, that there is still so much to do. Indeed, as there is no getting away from advanced disease or from the existential questions, the need will always be there. How amazing really, that those of us in the medical and allied professions had drifted so far and needed those pioneers to show us this essential truth.

Setting politics and finances aside (and unfortunately for Katharine House we cannot do either), there is a yet more challenging role for specialist palliative care in these days when the value of life and the timing of death are so hotly debated, if only to release people from the 'sick role' enabling them to be human again and to live more fully; to support them when things seem to be going awry or when they feel alone; to use expert skills to relieve them of their discomfort and help them make sense of life; to aid reconciliation and foster hope and, dare I say, to be one of those voices that speaks to the world of the everlasting nature of love.

I am glad this memoir has been published. It is inspiring to read such a story, and we need to be uplifted and inspired in this world. I hope too that the people of Banbury and beyond who have so generously helped to keep the Hospice running will come to appreciate both the great sacrifice and the great dedication which have been needed to create and maintain Katharine House.

THE LAST SONG

*"Fortune, when she has brought men to the height of her wheel,
is wont, either in jest or repentance, to bring them down again"*
Giorgio Vasari

*"O throat, O throbbing heart. And I singing hopelessly, hopelessly, all the
night"*
Walt Whitman

When Gulliver heard about the immortals of Laputa, he believed that he would
meet a race of people whose happiness would know no bounds as their minds
would be "without the weight and depression caused by the continual
apprehension of death". He was, as we know, wrong. They were in reality a
very miserable people.

We, who know that living forever is not part of the human condition, are not, I
think, much assailed by the contemplation of our own demise. We do know
that the death of others will impinge upon our lives but, insofar as we
anticipate bereavement, it will be concerned with those whom we have loved
the most from our own or earlier generations. We know that we will have to
come to terms with life's altered circumstances. We can only hope and have
endeavoured to ensure that, to whichever of us falls the lot of holding the other
dead, the sorrow will be diminished by the knowledge that the relationship was
good. We certainly do not contemplate the early death of a child. When that
does happen we are faced with what can be described as a defining moment in
life when one is forced out of a preoccupation with inessentials to a
confrontation with a deep and desperate reality. There is evidence which
shows that those who have lost a parent, a spouse and a child invariably
describe their grief for the child as the most enduring and difficult to survive.

Because we do not think about it, one's reaction to this frightening
circumstance cannot be predicted. One of my reactions was to write what
others have been kind enough to describe as elegiac poetry, for which I claim
no literary merit but which was highly cathartic and can be fully recommended
as a valuable activity in bereavement. Poetry has been used by many people
over the centuries to attempt to assuage the grief of bereavement. There are
countless examples of such writing from the Greeks and Romans onward.
"Pearl" , a lament for the death of a daughter, is a wonderful and moving

example of medieval writing in this circumstance. *"The Long Pale Corridor"* brings together much contemporary writing on the theme.

Grief is sometimes spoken of as a process but I believe that much more appropriate words are battle, struggle and contest. Grief caused by the early death of someone for whom one has had a loving responsibility can assail with anger, insidiously poison with guilt, make one subject to the stabbing pain of continuous reminders of the past and can weaken with the everlasting pain from the intangible wound of longing. At one end of the spectrum is the need to lament and at the other a mistily perceived greater reality which one struggles to reach. The healing power of time is uncertain and time passes slowly. My own writing was spontaneous:

Tears flood mind,
Pen is flotsam.
Cries black rivers
Of weeping words.

It was never intended for publication but I can now describe one of the countless acts of kindness to which I refer in the introduction to this book.

Jeff Jones, a very good friend and a graphic designer who had already presented Katharine House with its *friz quadrata* logo, suggested that publication of my writing would be worthwhile. With the help of his associates 1,000 copies of a slim volume were produced and much to my surprise almost all were sold within a year – to the benefit of the, then, almost empty coffers of the embryo hospice. In 1993 I was approached by the friend of a friend who was a freelance journalist. He had been commissioned by The Times to write a series of articles for the Education Supplement, exploring the activities of head teachers in retirement. When the article about Katharine House was published *"The Last Song"* was mentioned and again, much to my amazement, I received requests for copies from all over the world. More copies were needed to fulfil orders and this time the print workshop in the education department at Bullingdon Prison came to the rescue. We had already developed a relationship with the prison under a Home Office scheme and 500 copies of a slightly expanded version were produced.

I have appended here some extracts from *"The Last Song"* because of the very positive responses it received from two sources. In 1987 I was asked to participate in a *Help the Hospices* seminar on 'Arts in the Hospice'. My subject was, of course, writing in bereavement. I was not at all surprised to learn that few of my audience wrote poetry which is after all a minority activity. But the response to my writing from this group of professionals together with the many responses I received from the recipients of the book lead me to believe that for the significant minority of people who read poetry it has a deep significance.

Positively, poetry can be seen if not as a purge for grief then as an aid to experiencing it. Ordinary words seem to trivialise or contain whereas poetry reflects the multifarious moods, paradoxes, changes, inconsistencies and downright contradictions involved when we deal with deeply traumatic and wounding experiences and does so with feeling and honesty. Poetry can react too with the experience of the reader. It can be a comforting echo of the reader's own emotions, helping to show that certain emotions are not unique. In some cases it can fulfil the human need to follow in the footsteps of others, again giving the comfort of shared experience, or it can be a valuable insight into a place beyond personal experience. Perhaps too it might lead toward the acquisition of the greater maturity which can accept and share the pain of others and, in a broader way, it may stop the reader in his tracks and put into perspective what is the real value of life.

MUSIC WAS YOUR FOOD

Music was your food,
Each note a calorie to feed your heart
And, therein, nurture love,

To emerge from your skilled hands,
Through vibrant strings,
Bursting with aching joy…

The same joy that in your eyes
Hid from us all
Your longing to be free

Heaven's incomparable music feeds you now.
We have a triple epitaph.
Your silent violins

NO MORE WILL I WALK

No more will I walk
The gleaming sands of Mochras
Beside the dark seas broken edge
Or sift the tumbled shells for cowries.
Nor climb the steepest dunes,
Lips moist with the wild strawberries nectar,
Under the summer sky, easy of heart and carefree

No more will I tread
The hidden slopes of Rhinog
Under the moss-clad, perfumed oaks.
Or stalk the secret, fearful goats
Above the darkening Llyn,
Hands stained with the precious sap of bilberries,
On still Autumn days, easy of heart and carefree

No more will I steal
Close by the gentle Artro
To share the patient heron's vigil
And wonder at the dipper's plunge
Or lie in lazy sleep
Replete, beneath the brambles empty boughs,
With you beside me, easy of heart and carefree

MISCELLANY OF DREAMS

Awakening to a silver morning,
- Perhaps only a symbol of such a morning –
A man stirs in a strange land,
Daybreak bringing inexplicable images to the mind.

Hurrying through air on wings of peregrine swiftness,
Sleek and barbule perfect,
Magnolia fragrance on the wind
Mysterious music emanates from low haunched hills.
A reticent voice, singing, hovers in the ambient atmosphere.

The hunter's arrow, barbed and poisoned
Mist and acrid vapours.

Discord, broken strings, a raucous overture!

Love, love, do not go near the fearsome precipice.
Avoid the foaming waters which annihilate.
Do not confirm aseity by the unheard song.

Dawn's silver tunnel, telescopic, concentrates the vision.
A bank of yellow straw, a smiling baby lies asleep.
Time – how long? – and metamorphosis.
The straw decayed, the baby is a skull.

Transmogrified the skull is shining, laughing, singing.
Thus the symbol is the path of life explained.

SPAT UPON THE BEACH

Spat upon the beach
I am too numb to heed progress
Or the wrath of politicians.
Too hurt to understand the
Sequestration of the
Briefly interloping spirit.
Too afraid to look for meaning.
Ideals infected by discord;
Walled in with the unperfumed
Honey of solitude;
Hope I spurn,
But know that mountains will stand by me
And try to take comfort from the return of exiled leaves.

RECOLLECTION OF CHRISTMAS 1981

The silver Christmas tree
Reflects the shimmering light
And the tumbling sounds
Stroked from a violin
Echo and re-echo round its branches.
Deep in my armchair,
Pensive,
I wish to learn the source of all this joy.
Where is the key which unlocks your hand and eye,
Accelerates your pulse,

Drives feeling from the deft young fingers
Through ancient pine and maple,
Animating air to touch the silver magically?
As a grey, stoic man, too close to soil and stone,
I did not know.
Only now the sounds a memory can I guess at
Something beyond the glinting stars
And yet, as you have shown me, illuminating dawn's dim light,
As close as the silver Christmas tree.

WHEN EARTH IS CLAD

When earth is clad in winter's death
Or summer's burgeoning,
The haunting false reality of
Brief encounters
Turns living faces,
Misjudged through the unsettled dust of sorrow,
Into the vanished dead.
Spellbound,
I emanate a silent stream of love,
Illicitly,
To be destroyed by winter's cold complexity
Or summer's quickening truth.

SPRING

Sun's pitch
steepens
Frost hard ground, heat stirred, softens.
Down deep,
Embryo level.
Root hairs sense
The Earth-tilt Spring
And flowers grow on your grave.

ADVICE TO MEMORY

When the wounded bird flies through
Mind's dark undergrowth,
Retrospection, abandon all save the powerful
Flight of music's winged messenger
Spiralling heavenwards on taut sinews.

ROLLRIGHT

I remember a night
Not long ago
When we reverted to childhood
As the receding Sun
Left its last flourish
On the ancient stones
Which we had counted a hundred times
But were always wrong.

That night a power
Exuded from the reddened landscape
Touching our wind-refined spirits
Drawing us to the joyful horizon and beyond.

Looking now, at the pictures you made
I see an infant happiness recorded,
A magic future promising everything.
We did not know the mischief that was cast,
Locked in the secret memory of the stones.
We had counted a hundred times
And were always wrong.

THERE HAS BEEN NO LETTER

There has been no letter for five months
Someone must know your whereabouts.
You must have been seen
By people closing the curtains
As you walked down Roath hill to choir rehearsal.
Or, returning, by the bus driver at Pen-y-Lan.
You are easily recognisable,
The songs inside your head plain upon your face,
Your vibrant passing leaving a trail of light

No one could miss.
But though I travel from wild sea shore to desolate mountain
The voices of Morganwg are silent.
And still the postman passes.

LIFE FLOWS

Down a river of meandering time
Life flows,
Wearing the heavy weight of being mortal
Towards a destiny that only God
Can know

Through the wild, erratic winds of time,
Life falters,
Fearing the storms, that with discordant passion
Obscure the path, the journey and the
Goal

Under the transient, finite Sun
Life grows
Shedding the burden of the shallow mind,
To enter realms of timelessness and
Light

BWLCH TYDDIAD

To this place
We came to gather the wild bilberries
Here the landscape retains a patina of her presence
An evocation of yesterday.
Below, people are climbing the "Roman Steps"
With silent movements, their laughter silent too:
It finds me unreceptive
So slants away towards the hilltop.
Above, a solitary buzzard accentuates the isolation.
We found unity in the sky.
The green boughs offer their blue flecked promises
But a snake binds my arms and
My feet are one with granite.
The people pass.
The buzzard drifts away.

Night's ceiling, a wordless blue-black valediction,
Overgrows my sight.
There is no harvest

MOURN NO MORE

Mourn no more; she's left us for
The deep and dappled woodland
Where fox and badger, secretly,
Her progress contemplate
And the darting blackbird's cries
Arouse in her desire

No longer weep; her journey's on
The heather scented moorland
Where grazing ewes, sad faced,
Her purposes enquire,
While the loose winged, mewing buzzards
Coax her into flight

Mourn no more; she's climbing
To the lone mysterious mountain
Beyond whose crags the tumbling ravens
Greet the upward surge
And the whispering wind alone
Knows her intent

VIOLIN MUSIC

To you I was indebted
For my love of plaintive violins.
Short partings were easy,
The serenading strings returned
With your deft fingers
And your singing heart.
Now I am afraid of the highly strung sounds
Like a whiplash in the solar plexus.

BIRTHDAY AT A GRAVESIDE

Horse chestnut tree, guard well your charge,
The secret cache under your boughs where lies a dream.

Where did the dream begin?
In the abundance of light flooding the conception;
In the loving or in the birth turned death;
In those piercing eyes touched by stars or lightning;
Through melodious hands, emanating a new river's magic impulses;
Or in the heart beating a wordless therapy?
The dream is all, broken now into a thousand disjointed pieces.
And there is no easy waking, only a cruel concerto
Claimed by no known composer.
Only a storm of tears drowning in its own heartbreak.
Only a lonely road and a signpost to a
Secret cache under an old horse chestnut tree.
And yet, as ever in this quiet place, elegiac musings
Arouse the attenuated harmonics of a sweetly sung melody
And of love's impulses sensed through a glowing halo,
So that ephemerality and permanence are understood.

LINES WRITTEN IN BALSCOTE CHURCHYARD

To go forward is to abandon the past,
The fecund past, endlessly prolific
With gaiety and joy.
For there lived one who loved and laughed,
Made music, sang, created unique pictures
Through a mind which ranged the universe.
I was untroubled there,
Fortified by small certainties;
Shadowing footprints always trod the rippled sand.
Rhapsody and pastoral encompassed all
And an Angel's voice spoke tenderly
Filling the air with gladness.

Don't think I fashion an elegy in this quiet place,
For what is past is present and in the future.
There is a golden bridge for loneliness to cross
From this broken world to a realm beyond
Where memory is now, where souls can intermingle
And together are eternal, amaranthine.

ENVOI

I have been involved in Katharine House as a volunteer for more than twenty years and as the organisation comes of age with a velocity of its own, I can look back on a period of life which I did not anticipate and certainly did not seek. In the introduction to this book I emphasised the constructive, affirmative and positive experiences which I have had the good fortune to have as companions and which have made it easier to accept the turn of fate which altered the course of my life. Indeed there are times when I am even able to see the experience as having been a privilege. The reward, if any is deserved, is the knowledge that we are not the selfish unconnected people often portrayed in the media and the fact that Katharine House has become an integral part of a local community whose members seem to want it to continue. I am grateful for that.

Simone de Beauvoir, in her treatise on old age (a condition which I have not yet attained in spite of having had the opportunity to blow out seventy candles!), said that "there is only one solution if old age is not to be an absurd parody of our former life and that is to go on pursuing the ends that give our existence meaning". Twenty years is a long time to be Chairman of a hospice trust, some would say longer than is desirable, but I retain a passion, even an indignation, which will I hope enable me to continue to make a contribution to Katharine House.

I have tried to tell a story, but like the American Indian, Tananawis, feel that sometimes the story has told me. I am sure that it will continue to do so.